THE
ALLERGY-FREE
COOKBOOK

RECIPES FOR GOOD HEALTH

THE
ALLERGY-FREE
COOKBOOK

Written and compiled by

Danila Armstrong, SRD, and Dr Andrew Cant

OCTOPUS BOOKS

ACKNOWLEDGMENTS

The publisher acknowledges the following photographers: Bryce Attwell page 96; Laurie Evans page 112; Robert Golden page 43; Melvin Grey pages 70, 75; John Lee page 32; Norman Nicholls pages 50–1; Roger Phillips pages 28–9, 78–9, 81; Clive Street pages 38–9; Grant Symon cover, pages 2–3, 58–9, 63, 85, 88–9, 93, 101, 104, 108–9; Paul Williams pages 35, 36. The Californian Raisin Advisory Bureau supplied the photograph on page 67, and the US Rice Council the photograph on page 55. Cookware, dishes and cutlery used in Grant Symon's photographs were provided by: Bella Figura, 154 Fulham Road, London SW10; Graham and Green, 4 and 7 Elgin Crescent, London W11; Neal Street East, Neal Street, London WC1; and Rosenthal Studio Haus, 102 Brompton Road, London SW3.

The energy and fibre values included in the recipes were based on information supplied by GF Dietary Group of Companies, Holland and Barrett Ltd and Rite-Diet Welfare Foods Ltd, and on information from *The Composition of Foods* by R.A. McCance and E.M. Widdowson, 4th revised edition, HMSO 1978, by A.A. Paul and D.A.T. Southgate, and from the second supplement to *The Composition of Foods* by S.P.Taw, R.W. Wenlock and D.H. Buss.

The recipe for Egg-free mayonnaise on page 118 was supplied by the G.F. Dietary Group of Companies.

The authors wish to thank their friends and colleagues Pat Bacon, Janet Bailes, Penny Hull, Peter Kilshaw and Valerie Neild for their help and encouragement.

Cover illustration: Pears in cassis (page 77), Pork Olivier with apple sauce (page 47) and mangetout. Title spread illustration: Tropical fruit salad (page 82), Lamb on skewers (page 45).

COOKING NOTE

Frequent references are made to special products in the recipes. Readers should refer to the following pages for the text notes on these products:

Egg replacers, page 22; milk substitutes, pages 21–2; special breads/breadcrumbs, the recipes on pages 88–9; special margarines, page 22.

CONTENTS

FOOD ALLERGY IN PERSPECTIVE

There is increasing interest in the role of food allergy in disease, especially among members of the public and practitioners of alternative or complementary medicine. Many orthodox medical practitioners dismiss the potential link between disease and allergy because of inconclusive evidence and the exaggerated and extravagant claims sometimes made; hence patients receive different advice according to whether they consult 'believers' or 'unbelievers'. The result is that some people with food-allergic disease are not properly diagnosed and treated, while others are put on diets dangerously deficient in vital nutrients for conditions that may or may not have anything to do with what they eat.

We believe that reactions to specific foods can cause a wide range of disorders, though food allergy is not the cause of every symptom. First, we briefly describe the conditions that can be shown to be caused by food allergy, as well as mentioning those where the link with diet is still uncertain. We then give advice on the best way to show up suspected allergies, together with an explanation of how they can

be diagnosed and treated using properly constructed exclusion diets on which you will avoid potential problem foods. We have taken great care to ensure that our exclusion diets remain safe and nutritionally adequate provided they are only followed for the recommended time.

Discovering which foods provoke reactions and eliminating them is only half the answer if it leaves you with a monotonous and uninspiring diet. The remainder of the book aims to provide a wide range of interesting and nutritious recipes suitable for different occasions. In addition, there is help in understanding food labels, advice on the basic ingredients to buy for home cooking, and information on how to wean the baby born into an allergy-prone family.

A word of caution before we begin: before undertaking any dietary measures for a suspected food allergy – whether for yourself or your children – please pay particular attention to the introductory section, 'Are you a suitable candidate for our exclusion diets?', to the four-stage food allergy plan on pages 14–15.

WHAT IS FOOD ALLERGY?

The word allergy causes much confusion. When first coined 80 years ago it described any response by the body's immune defence system, including reactions against germs, such as bacteria and viruses. More recently it has been used to talk about harmful overreactions of the immune system, especially when directed at innocuous substances like pollen or animal fur, or foods such as egg or cows' milk. Today it

is widely used as a term for an unpleasant reaction to almost any substance, whether the immune system is involved or not.

Strictly speaking, the term allergy should be reserved for responses made by the immune system. Other adverse reactions to things we eat should really be called food intolerance, as has recently been recommended by the working party on food allergy set up by the Royal College of

Physicians and the British Nutrition Foundation. It is probably wise not to try to define these terms too rigidly as the ways in which allergy and intolerance develop are not yet well understood, and diseases thought to be caused by one may turn out to be caused by the other. Furthermore the two terms are often used interchangeably in both the medical and lay press.

True food allergy is more common in children than adults and in people who suffer (or have at some time suffered) from eczema, asthma or hayfever, as well as those who are from families with a strong incidence of these ailments. These people produce abnormally large amounts of an antibody in their bloodstream called IgE, particularly in response to certain foods, pollens and animal hair. This raised level of IgE is responsible for immediate reactions such as hives (or urticaria), which appear on the body within minutes of contact with the offending food. Such people are also more prone to delayed reactions to food which develop some hours after they have eaten the food and may be manifest as eczema, asthma, migraine, joint pain or vomiting and diarrhoea.

The exact physical mechanism for these responses is not yet well understood, but the IgE antibody is probably not the main cause. Food intolerance can occur in a number of ways. Sometimes chemical substances in the foods directly cause these reactions. Caffeine in tea and coffee; tyramine in cheese, yeast and red wine; and histamine in beer, cheese, chocolate and canned fish can provoke a wide range of symptoms including migraine, attacks of flushing, hives and diarrhoea. On other occasions foods (tomatoes and strawberries in particular) cause the body itself to release histamine into the bloodstream which in turn causes symptoms.

Susceptibility to these various naturally occurring chemicals differs from individual to individual, though the precise reasons why one person reacts and another does not remain unclear. Some people develop food intolerance because they cannot digest and utilize certain food components. This is usually because they lack a special substance in their digestive system called an enzyme. Thus people who lack the enzyme to digest lactose (the sugar in milk) get diarrhoea when they drink cows' milk, because of its sugar content (see page 10).

Finally it must be remembered that a psychological aversion to a food can produce quite dramatic physical symptoms. Researchers have revealed this quite simply by giving the offending food to volunteer patients in a disguised form. If the food intolerance is caused by a psychological aversion, the disguised food will not provoke any symptoms.

CONDITIONS SOMETIMES CAUSED BY FOOD ALLERGY

SKIN DISORDERS

URTICARIA This common condition, also known as hives, is seen in all age groups but particularly in young children. Around one in ten children born into allergy-prone families will be affected by food-induced urticaria. This condition is commonest from weaning until the second birthday. Fortunately most children grow out of it after this age, although some will continue to be affected throughout life.

White fluid-filled lumps rapidly appear on the skin, often resembling nettle-rash. These lumps have a red margin and come up where there has been direct contact with the offending substance. When a food is to blame, the lips and face swell up and a curious tingling sensation is felt in the mouth. Usually only one or two foods are to blame, eggs and cows' milk being the ones most commonly implicated, but colourings, preservatives, nuts, fish, wheat and other foods may also be responsible. Urticaria is one of the most common of all food allergies.

Urticarial reactions usually occur within seconds or minutes of eating or coming into contact with the food and are a good example of the immediate type of allergy caused by IgE antibodies. IgE antibodies are not always involved, though, and drugs like aspirin can also trigger off urticaria. It has also been found that general factors such as warmth, exercise and emotion can lower the threshold at which food-induced urticaria occurs.

People who develop urticaria should recall all the foods they have eaten during the hour or two prior to the reaction, as offending foods can usually be identified and eliminated from the diet in this way. For some people, though, it may not be so simple to track down the culprit foods; research suggests that food preservatives and colourings such as tartrazine are often responsible in these cases.

ECZEMA Also known as atopic dermatitis, this can be a very distressing and persistent condition, and although particularly common in preschool children – affecting around one in ten of the under-fives – it can arise at any age and is becoming more common. Typically an itchy red rash appears, most often on the face and on the skin behind the knees and inside the elbows, though it may be more extensive. The skin becomes thickened or cracked, often weeping and bleeding.

The last decade has produced some valuable research on the link between diet and eczema, and it now seems clear that some, though unfortunately not all, eczema sufferers show a definite improvement when they avoid specific foods. Though the figures are still in dispute, it appears that 50 per cent of children, and a rather smaller proportion of adult eczema sufferers may respond to dietary measures.

Identification of the offending foods is not as easy as in urticaria. Food-induced eczema often does not become apparent until the food has been taken regularly for several days, and several different foods may all be implicated in provoking the condition (see page 12). Carefully planned dietary measures – such as those described later in this book – are therefore needed to identify and eliminate the offending foods.

In many cases the effect of proper dietary measures is so dramatic that other treatment is no longer needed; while for others, an allergy-free diet will improve the condition significantly but prescribed medications will still be required. In some cases, though, the benefits from dietary measures will be too small to make avoiding certain foods worthwhile.

RESPIRATORY DISORDERS

ASTHMA This is another extremely common ailment, affecting around 10 per cent of children and a smaller proportion of adults. It is characterized by coughing, wheezing and difficulty in breathing. Dust, pollens and virus infections most commonly trigger asthmatic attacks, but in one study 17 per cent of asthmatics found that foods also induced an attack, and in another report one-third appeared to suffer from food-allergic asthma.

Sometimes an attack occurs after eating the offending food, but on other occasions merely its smell is sufficient. This shows how an allergic reaction can sometimes be triggered by very small amounts of a substance. Many different foods have been reported to provoke attacks, but aspirin and food additives such as tartrazine, metabisulphite, benzoate and monosodium glutamate seem to be most often involved.

Careful reading of food labelling is obviously vital when planning an allergy-free diet for an asthmatic.

It is most important to remember that food allergy is rarely the sole trigger factor in asthma. Although appropriate dietary measures may greatly improve the overall condition, reducing the frequency of attacks, it is essential to continue with any prescribed medication, under your doctor's supervision, as other trigger factors may continue to cause problems.

RHINITIS The symptoms of this condition are the runny, snuffly nose experienced by many people prone to allergies. Hay fever (or seasonal rhinitis) is one form, though this occurs only in the pollen season during the spring and summer months. But pollen is not the only trigger, and some cases can be provoked by either eating or smelling a food, the most common culprit being egg.

BOWEL DISORDERS

There are several different bowel disorders in which food allergy seems to play a part, though the physical mechanisms for these reactions are not well understood. Vomiting, diarrhoea and stomach ache, sometimes with urticaria can occur after eating foods such as shellfish, egg or cows' milk. Usually symptoms come on within a few hours of eating the culprit food and disappear after a few more.

In these circumstances the diagnosis of food allergy is not difficult, but in other conditions it is less easy to find the link with diet, either because several food allergies coexist, or because the food substance in question is found in many foods and the correct exclusion diet has not been devised.

Sometimes food allergy is only one of the factors involved and this too can add to the confusion. A number of specific bowel disorders appear sometimes to be related to food allergy and these are described next.

IRRITABLE BOWEL SYNDROME This is a common syndrome in adults, particularly in women, and as many as 30 per cent of the population are affected by it at some time. In a typical case there is severe cramp-like stomach ache, with diarrhoea or alternating episodes of diarrhoea and constipation. A recent study found that 75 per cent of patients significantly improved when specific foods were removed from their diets. On careful reintroduction of these foods it was found that wheat, corn, dairy products, citrus fruits, tea and coffee most often exacerbated this condition.

INFLAMMATORY BOWEL DISEASE This term is used to cover two separate conditions, both of which mainly affect young adults: ulcerative colitis and Crohn's disease. The former is a disease of the large bowel characterized by bloody diarrhoea and, in more severe cases, general weakness. Various researchers have suggested that foods are involved in the development of this condition, and cows' milk in particular has been implicated. Except in the case of young children (in whom ulcerative colitis is very rare) most recent data suggest that food allergy is *not* an important factor.

Crohn's disease, on the other hand, involves the small bowel and gives rise to more variable symptoms, which include stomach ache, diarrhoea and weight loss, and are usually first noticed in young adulthood. It is becoming more common, though the reason for this and the cause of the disease remain obscure.

Four years ago an allergy-free diet was tried on a patient with Crohn's disease who was mistakenly thought to have the irritable bowel syndrome. She improved dramatically and since then other patients with Crohn's disease have been reported to benefit from such a diet. It is too early to assess these findings properly, but food allergy or intolerance may well be important here.

People who have had this condition diagnosed should only try the exclusion diets in this book under the supervision of their doctor and dietitian as they may be undernourished and need special supplements.

COELIAC DISEASE This disorder is less common than most of those already described, affecting one or two in a thousand, but it is important to include it here as it has been shown to be unequivocally diet-related.

Gluten, which is present in small quantities in wheat, oats, rye and barley flour, damages the surface of the coeliac disease sufferer's small bowel, preventing proper digestion and absorption of food. This leads to weight loss, diarrhoea and vitamin deficiencies.

Coeliac disease often becomes apparent early in life, 50 per cent of sufferers being diagnosed before the age of three years. In some people the symptoms are less obvious and they may not discover they have the condition until later in life.

A link with diet was suspected for many years, but only finally proven in Holland during the famine of 1945. At this time flour was unobtainable and so potatoes became the staple food. Surprisingly, people with coeliac disease improved remarkably, and the link with gluten was then established. Even small amounts of gluten can cause problems and gluten is found in many foods.

Diagnosis and treatment by a specialist

doctor with expert advice from a dietitian are most important. Diagnosed coeliacs and those who think they may have coeliac disease should *not* follow our exclusion diets described later in the book. However, people with coeliac disease can use any of our gluten-free recipes which are marked with the symbol: Ⓖ. But it should be noted that recipes with the wheat-free symbol Ⓦ which do not also have the gluten-free symbol must be avoided. This is because some wheat-free recipes contain other gluten-containing cereals, such as rye.

Happily, once you are on a gluten-free diet, the symptoms of coeliac disease will disappear completely.

COWS' MILK ALLERGY (CMA) This is also known as cows' milk protein intolerance or cows' milk sensitive enteropathy, and it mainly affects babies in the first year of life — around two in every hundred — more commonly those who have been bottle-fed. Symptoms often start after an episode of gastroenteritis and include vomiting, diarrhoea, colic and poor weight gain. Sometimes these infants also suffer from eczema and rhinitis (see above).

Fortunately most babies grow out of this condition, but a paediatrician should be consulted to make sure they are not suffering from some other bowel disorder unrelated to allergy.

If CMA is diagnosed, cows' milk in all forms should be excluded from the diet, and an alternative baby soya milk formula given (*not* ordinary soya milk, which is nutritionally inadequate for babies). These measures invariably result in a complete and rapid cure.

After some months cows' milk may carefully be reintroduced, preferably in a hospital clinic in case there are any untoward reactions.

LACTOSE INTOLERANCE Lactose is the sugar naturally occurring in milk. The enzyme necessary to digest lactose is present at birth, but sometimes disappears after baby-hood. This is particularly common in people of African and West Indian descent. The symptoms of this complaint are a swollen stomach and diarrhoea, occurring soon after a more-than-modest amount of milk has been drunk.

Lactose intolerance is probably commoner than is realized, because many people with this condition do not bother to consult their doctor, but instinctively get into the habit of not drinking too much milk.

In adults, if the symptoms cease when you stop drinking too much milk, there is no need to consult a doctor. If you suspect that your child has lactose intolerance, he or she should be seen by your doctor, who may prescribe a soya milk formula as a replacement for milk.

As far as is known, there are no serious long-term effects of lactose intolerance.

MIGRAINE

This is a common condition, affecting, among others, one in five women of child-bearing age and one in twenty older children. The term has different meanings for different people, and so it is hard to give a precise definition. It usually refers to episodes of recurrent headache, felt more on one side of the head than the other, and the pain often has a throbbing quality. An attack usually lasts for several hours and is sometimes accompanied by nausea and vomiting. Many migraine sufferers complain that bright light hurts their eyes and some have visual symptoms, such as seeing little bright dots in front of their eyes; they may also look rather pale during an attack.

The ancient Greek physician Hippocrates first suggested a link between certain foods and migraine, and recommended that those suffering from headaches should avoid milk and heavy wine. In recent times fish, alcohol, chocolate and milk products are most often implicated, though to what extent migraine sufferers are affected by diet is as yet unknown. In a recent study, 90 per cent of children with severe migraine were free of symptoms if they followed a vigorous exclusion diet. Symptoms returned after they took certain foods, usually three or four different ones, but in one extreme case headaches were triggered by as many as 20 different foods.

Tracking down such allergies requires expert help, and it may be that this is why· some food allergies remain undetected. Whether such a high proportion of migraine sufferers in general would benefit from exclusion diets is not yet known; clearly, further research work is needed.

In the light of current medical knowledge, we believe that if migraine has been diagnosed and is making your life a misery, it is worth trying our food-allergy plan described later in the book. It can do you no harm and if it helps you to track down and eliminate culprit foods from your diet, it may well pay dividends.

If your child has had migraine diagnosed and you want to try dietary measures, please read pages 14–15 before taking any steps in this direction.

HYPERACTIVITY

Hyperactive children are restless, excitable and easily distracted and frustrated. They sleep poorly at night and are often aggressive. Around 2–5 per cent of children are hyperactive, with a ratio of six boys to one girl. Understandably they cause considerable anxiety to their parents and teachers.

Hyperactive behaviour in children has been associated with dietary factors for several years. At first hyperactivity was attributed by some experts to aspirin-like chemicals occurring naturally in foods such as tomatoes and citrus fruits, together with colourings and preservatives. In an attempt to normalize hyperactive behaviour some of these children were put on diets excluding these suspect substances. Although some improved, many doctors and psychologists remained sceptical of any link between diet and hyperactivity.

During 1984 and 1985, however, a very thorough study of severely hyperactive children was carried out in London, and the results surprised even the doctors involved. Almost without exception their behaviour was much better when they took a very rigorous, medically supervised exclusion diet (the oligo-allergenic diet mentioned on page 13). Most then became hyperactive again after eating specific foods, usually several different foods in each case. Although colourings and preservatives were most often responsible, no child reacted to these alone.

Very careful dietary investigation is needed to uncover such reactions and must be carried out under the supervision of a doctor and/or dietitian. Due to the complexity of the potential food reactions involved, it is probable that one of the more rigorous exclusion diets mentioned on page 13 will be recommended.

To sum up, further research work is still needed to clarify and confirm the findings of the recent London study, but food allergy may well prove to be a signficant factor in hyperactivity.

THE LINK BETWEEN FOOD ALLERGY AND OTHER DISEASES

As with any new and popular topic in medicine, many claims have been made, and some are proving to be unfounded. Usually they concern diseases which are distressing and disabling and for which conventional treatment is not of great benefit. Multiple sclerosis (a paralysing disease of the nervous system) is one such condition, and to date there is little scientific evidence that exclusion diets are of benefit or that food allergy plays a part in causing the disease.

The same is true for rheumatoid arthritis, a painful progressive disease affecting the body's joints. Some food-allergic people do get swollen and painful joints, but this is unusual and does not involve lasting damage, as in rheumatoid arthritis.

Severe mental disorders, such as schizophrenia, have also been said to be due to food allergy, but little has been found to support these assertions.

SUMMARY OF FOOD-ALLERGY-RELATED CONDITIONS

Below are the ailments most often related to food allergy, together with the foods most commonly implicated in each condition. Remember that several foods may be responsible and we have listed only the foods most likely to be involved, not all those that may be involved.

URTICARIA	Eggs, cows' milk and its products, colourings, preservatives, nuts, seafood, wheat, strawberries, tomatoes, alcohol and aspirin.
ECZEMA	Cows' milk and its products, eggs, colourings, preservatives, chocolate, citrus fruit and wheat.
ASTHMA AND RHINITIS	Cows' milk and its products; additives such as monosodium glutamate, sulphur dioxide, metabisulphites and benzoic acid; wheat and aspirin.
IRRITABLE BOWEL SYNDROME	Wheat, corn, cows' milk and its products, citrus fruit, tea and coffee.
CROHN'S DISEASE	Wheat, cows' milk and its products, corn and yeast.
COELIAC DISEASE	Gluten-containing foods: wheat, rye, barley and oats.
COWS' MILK ALLERGY	Cows' milk and its products.
LACTOSE INTOLERANCE	Cows', goats' and ewes' milk and most of their products.
MIGRAINE	Cows' milk and milk products, fish, alcohol, chocolate and caffeine (in coffee, tea, cola drinks, etc.).
HYPERACTIVITY	Colourings, preservatives, cows' milk and its products, citrus fruits, chocolate and wheat.

HOW FOOD ALLERGIES ARE DIAGNOSED

A number of special medical tests have been devised to detect allergy to foods, but none is completely satisfactory.

Skin-prick testing is carried out by gently pricking a food extract into the skin and seeing if a small area of urticaria develops. This is quick and painless and if large responses are seen, they usually predict foods causing urticaria. However, as urticaria follows very quickly after eating the offending food, the culprit is usually obvious and a test unnecessary.

Specific blood tests give much the same information as skin-prick tests and neither reveals which foods are provoking conditions such as eczema or migraine when a food allergy is involved.

Other tests such as the pulse test, the sublingual test and cytotoxic testing have not stood up well to scientific study. Less orthodox forms of testing such as radionics, radiesthensia, psionic medicine and dousing seem to be based on belief rather than science.

As yet the only reliable way to detect a food allergy is to remove all potentially allergy-provoking foods from the diet and then reintroduce them one by one, seeing which cause a reappearance or worsening of the condition.

THE FOUR-STAGE FOOD ALLERGY PLAN

We have devised this plan to help you find out whether your symptoms are food allergy-related and, if so, to enable you to isolate the culprit foods and eliminate them from your diet. We shall begin by outlining the general principles of exclusion diets, and move on to the details of how to put them into practice on page 15.

Of course, if you already know you are allergic to certain foods, such as shellfish or strawberries, you will be able to avoid them without any trouble. But if you suspect that you might be food-allergic and are not sure which foods trigger your symptoms, the first stage is to keep a food diary. By keeping a careful note of what you eat and when your symptoms occur, you may be able to pinpoint certain culprit foods, which you should then try to avoid.

If these measures are unsuccessful the second stage is to exclude a wider range of potential allergy-provoking foods from your diet – in other words, follow our suggested exclusion diet(s). These require great attention to detail and particular care in checking the ingredients of packaged foods, which often contain unexpected additives.

The third stage is the gradual reintroduction into your diet of the excluded foods. As you reintroduce the foods one by one, you will be able to see exactly which ones cause your symptoms.

The fourth and final stage is to plan a diet that avoids the foods you are allergic to, and is at the same time nutritionally balanced and appetizing.

FURTHER OPTIONS

Although our exclusion diets stand a very good chance of identifying the foods you are allergic to, they do not eliminate all potential problem foods and if your symptoms persist, it is possible for you to pursue your quest for culprit foods further under medical supervision.

1 Your doctor and/or dietitian may suggest an oligo-allergenic diet ('*oligos*' being ancient Greek for 'few'), which limits you to as few foods as possible, allowing only one meat, one starchy food, one vegetable and one fruit, together with distilled or mineral water and vitamin and mineral supplements. It does need professional supervision and should be undertaken only if your symptoms do not respond to other treatment and if they are more irksome than is the diet itself.

2 In exceptional circumstances your doctor may advise an elemental diet. This is a liquid diet that contains all the essential nutrients in particles too small to provoke an allergic response. It is an expensive treatment and can be carried out only in a hospital or clinic.

3 The most extreme form of treatment in the quest for food allergies is fasting, and this too may only safely be attempted in hospital.

Although fasting and the stricter diets are more likely to unmask food allergies, they are more difficult to stick to than our exclusion diets, the reintroduction of foods takes longer, and they always need medical and dietetic supervision.

ARE YOU A SUITABLE CANDIDATE FOR OUR EXCLUSION DIETS?

Before you embark on our basic or stricter exclusion diets, you should check with your doctor that your symptoms are due to the condition you suspect. Once he or she has confirmed that you have eczema, irritable bowel syndrome, or any of the other conditions described previously, you should also check that dietary measures are not unwise for health reasons. You may be advised against making changes in your diet if you are suffering from other complaints in addition to the one you suspect may be food allergy-related. In most cases you will be told that it is safe to try the exclusion diet on your own, but some people need medical supervision (see below).

If you are taking any medication, ask your doctor if you can have a break from it during the food testing period. Many medicines contain colourings, preservatives and food fillers such as lactose and wheat starch, to which you may be allergic. Alternatives can be prescribed for some medicines. Bear in mind, too, that many vitamin, mineral and tonic preparations also contain additives. It goes without saying that you should never change a prescribed medication routine without consulting your doctor.

If possible, stop smoking for the period of your dietary testing because of its adverse effects on many of the body's functions. Smoking could make interpreting the effect of the exclusion diet difficult.

THOSE REQUIRING MEDICAL SUPERVISION

COELIAC DISEASE Coeliacs should *not* follow our exclusion diets. If you suffer from coeliac disease, your doctor or dietitian will prescribe a special diet for you.

Our gluten-free recipes will, however, be suitable for inclusion in this diet. These are marked with the symbol Ⓖ. As already mentioned, recipes marked with the wheat-free symbol Ⓦ are not necessarily suitable for coeliacs, as many other cereals, such as rye, also contain gluten.

CROHN'S DISEASE People suffering from Crohn's disease are usually in a nutritionally poor condition. Under medical supervision they may be put on a diagnostic elemental diet (see page 13). Our diagnostic exclusion diets may be suitable for people with Crohn's disease but may only be tried under a doctor's or dietitian's supervision. Subsequently, if a specific food or foods, such as wheat, is confirmed to be involved in causing symptoms, the appropriately coded recipes in this book can be used.

HYPERACTIVITY Hyperactive children can have diagnostic exclusion diets prescribed specially for them by their doctors. Thus they should only be put on the exclusion diets in this book under the supervision of their doctor and dietitian. Once their cul-prit foods have been identified they can be given the appropriately labelled recipes in this book, all of which are free from artificial colourings, preservatives and flavourings.

DIABETES If you are diabetic, our exclusion diets are suitable for you, but as with all major changes in your diet, they will need to be undertaken under the supervision of your dietitian.

UNDER-18-YEAR-OLDS Anyone who is growing needs more of certain nutrients, such as calcium, than an adult, and serious and irreversible damage can result to babies and young children if they are put on abnormal diets. The exclusion diets we recommend *can* be used for children, but *only* under the supervision of a doctor or dietitian sympathetic to the idea of using dietary measures in the diagnosis of food-allergic conditions.

The only exception to this rule is if you suspect your child or youngster is allergic to just one or two foods (*except* milk). In this case the suspect food or foods can be excluded without medical supervision. This applies only to children over the age of two years, whose symptoms have been confirmed by the doctor to be associated with one of the food allergy-related conditions described previously, and whose doctor agrees that dietary measures won't have adverse effects on the child's health.

The appropriate recipes in this book can, however, be used for all children whose food allergy has been established by their doctor. Remember that for children milk is an important part of their diet and if this is excluded, suitable milk substitutes must be given (see pages 21–2).

Advice on weaning potentially allergic babies can be found on page 24.

STAGE 1: KEEPING A FOOD DIARY

If you are fairly certain that a particular food, or foods, is responsible for triggering your symptoms, you can skip the first two stages of our diet plan. Simply exclude the suspect food from your diet for three weeks and if your symptoms clear up or improve significantly, proceed to stage 3, the reintroduction, on page 19.

If, on the other hand, your symptoms remain unchanged after three weeks of excluding suspect foods, or you are not sure what foods might be responsible for your condition, start the four-stage food allergy plan by eating your normal diet and keeping a food diary. List everything you eat and drink, and the time at which they were consumed, and make a note of your symptoms when they occur, giving them a score on a point scale from 1–10 according to their severity. Your object is to spot possible links between food and symptoms, so brief notes of symptoms and the times at which they occur are sufficient. Remember to note everything, including medicines, sweets, drinks and snacks.

For commercially prepared foods you need to note the brand and either record the ingredients or, if unsure about what they contain, keep the labels to refer to later.

You should make a note too of weather conditions and changes in washing powder and toiletries – toothpaste, for example, (only use white toothpaste and avoid swallowing any).

If your doctor has agreed that dietary measures are appropriate for your child, keep the diary yourself, noting down the symptoms that are obvious to you. It is better not to tell your child about the diary, nor to ask him or her to tell you about any symptoms they may experience.

Keep your diary for a month then check through your notes. If you are allergic to only a few foods and eat them rarely, the offenders will soon become apparent. The length of time between eating the food and the onset of symptoms will vary from a matter of minutes to several days, depending on the condition. The longer the delay, the more difficult it is to pinpoint the culprit food or foods. How long reactions continue will also vary.

If by keeping a diary a pattern emerges and you can identify one or more troublemakers, omit these from your diet for a period of two to three weeks and see if your symptoms clear up or are significantly reduced. If they are, then go on to the reintroduction stage, page 19. If you observe no change in your condition, or you cannot identify the culprit foods by checking the relationship of foods and symptoms in your diary, then you will need to go on to stage 2.

STAGE 2: THE EXCLUSION DIETS

THE BASIC EXCLUSION DIET

This diet avoids the foods that many researchers have found commonly provoke allergies: cows' milk, eggs, beef and chicken (because of their respective association with milk and eggs), fish, wheat, citrus fruits, berry fruits, nuts, chocolate, tea, coffee, alcohol, colourings and preservatives.

From the outset you will appreciate that this is not going to be easy. But the overwhelming majority of our patients have managed to complete the three-week diet after careful preparation and planning.

BEFORE YOU START To help ensure a smooth transition on to the basic exclusion diet, start your initial planning at least two weeks in advance.

1 Look at the diet guidelines on page 17. If there are any foods in the allowed section that you know already upset you, avoid them.

2 Make a list of the foods and drinks that you will need on the diet. Be prepared for it to be rather expensive initially – some of the foodstuffs need to be bought from specialist shops.

3 Check through the recipes in this book for those suitable for the basic exclusion diet. They have the symbol ⊗.

4 For ideas on how to fit the recipes into a day-to-day eating plan, see the meal plans on pages 120–3.

5 Decide on a few recipes to try out before starting on the diet. The foods that will seem most different will be baked foods such as bread, cakes and biscuits, because you will be using unusual flour mixtures in their preparation.

6 If you have a freezer, it is a good idea to stock up in advance with baked goods and some pre-prepared meals, especially if you are used to relying on convenient commercially prepared foods. Once on the diet, if you are pressed for time, you will always have a store of suitable food to rely on.

7 Warn your friends, family, colleagues at work and neighbours not to put pressure on you to eat forbidden foods. Choose a time to try your diet when you are not due to attend lots of social functions or to go on holiday. The best time for children to try a new diet is during the holidays, unless you are allowed to provide packed lunches to be eaten at school.

8 Continue keeping your diary.

ON THE DIET Now you will appreciate all the work you have put in up to this point.

1 Stay on the diet for three weeks – no more and no less.

2 Continue to keep your food diary.

3 Don't give up! If you don't stick to your diet you will have wasted all your earlier efforts and you will have to start again.

4 If the foods you have excluded are responsible for your symptoms, you may start to notice an improvement towards the end of your second week. Eat as wide a variety of the allowed foods as possible. This should bring to light any unusual allergies or intolerances to the allowed foods, since setbacks are likely to be due to something you ate in the previous 24–48 hours (provided you don't put yourself at risk in any other way, for instance by visiting a house with a dog if you are asthmatic and your attacks are triggered by animal hair).

5 If new symptoms, such as weight loss or constipation, arise once you are on the exclusion diet, see page 18 for advice. If they are not covered there, consult your doctor.

6 If after three weeks you do not notice any significant changes in your symptoms, it is unlikely that food is the cause of your condition. It is possible, though, that the basic exclusion diet still contains food that you are allergic to. In which case you may like to try our stricter exclusion diet (see page 18). It is perfectly safe to begin this diet as soon as you have finished the first one.

7 If you do notice significant improvements after three weeks on the basic exclusion diet then it is likely that your symptoms can be controlled or improved in the long term by careful avoidance of the offending food or foods.

8 Go on to stage 3, the reintroduction (page 19).

BASIC EXCLUSION DIET GUIDELINES You may use the recipes from the book with the symbol ⊗, as well as the foods in the allowed list opposite. Refer to pages 20–1 for information on shopping for allowed alternatives to foods you should avoid and for advice on recognizing forbidden foods that aren't immediately obvious as such. See also the appendix on page 124 listing additives (and their E numbers) that are thought not to be involved in food-allergic reactions.

BASIC EXCLUSION DIET GUIDELINES

	FOODS ALLOWED	FOODS TO AVOID
MEAT	Lamb, pork, turkey, duck, rabbit, hare, venison and other game, and the offal from these meats.	Beef, chicken, ham, bacon, smoked meats, tinned meats, bought sausages and sausagemeat, preserved meats and bought meat dishes.
FISH	None.	All, including shellfish.
MILK AND MILK PRODUCTS	Milk substitutes (see pages 21–2), tofu.	Milk and milk products: butter, cream, yogurt, cheese, goats' milk and yogurt, ewes' milk, and foods with any of these included (pages 21–2).
EGGS	Egg replacer (see page 22).	Eggs, ducks' eggs, quails' eggs and foods containing egg, such as cakes and custard.
FATS	Special margarines (see page 22), sunflower oil, corn oil, olive oil, soya oil.	Ordinary margarines, lard, dripping, vegetable oils, suet.
VEGETABLES	All fresh and frozen; check ingredients if canned.	Dried, instant mashed potato, preprepared potatoes and some canned vegetables.
FRUIT	Most fresh fruits; if canned check ingredients. Wash all fresh fruit well.	Citrus fruits (oranges, lemons, grapefruits, limes, satsumas, etc), berry fruits (strawberries, blackberries, raspberries, loganberries, etc).
CEREALS	Corn, rice, oats, barley, rye, sago, buckwheat, millet, and flours made from these grains; cornflakes, Rice Krispies, potato flour, gram flour, Rite-Diet and Aglutella pasta (see page 123).	Wheat, wheat flour and all its products (bread, pastry, cakes, biscuits, pasta, etc); wheat-based breakfast cereals; thickened foods and sauces.
DRINKS	Pure apple juice, pineapple juice and other pure juices of permitted fruits (check ingredients); mineral waters, soda water, some herb teas, chicory and camomile tea, tomato juice.	Fizzy drinks, all squashes, alcohol, tea, coffee, cocoa-based drinks, most bedtime drinks, orange and grapefruit juice, lemon juice.
MISCELLANEOUS	Carob, salt and pepper, herbs, pure spices, jams of permitted fruits (check ingredients), honey, sugar, syrup and treacle (in moderation).	Chocolate, meat extracts, stock cubes, gravy mixes, gelatine, jelly, sweets, spreads, most colourings and preservatives (see page 124).

THE STRICTER EXCLUSION DIET

This is in essence the same as the basic exclusion diet already described, and may be followed if your symptoms remain unchanged after three weeks on the basic diet. You should begin the stricter diet without a break after the basic exclusion diet, and should continue the stricter diet *for no more than two weeks*.

On the stricter diet you have also to avoid:

- Potatoes
- Oats
- Barley
- Rye
- Corn
- Corn oil
- Glucose syrups
- Sweetcorn
- Popcorn
- Tap water
- Yeast

You can use any of the recipes in the book marked with ⊗ symbol.

Your main starchy foods will be rice, rice flour, rice-based breakfast cereals, rice cakes and millet. Try making the flatbread recipe on page 87 with gram flour instead of the maize flour. Use mineral water instead of tap water. The sparkling mineral waters Perrier and Prewett's, and the still mineral waters Volvic, Highland Spring and Evian, have the lowest salt content, and are therefore healthier.

If after trying the stricter diet, there is still no change in your condition, go back to normal eating and see your doctor, who may be able to suggest whether more extreme medically supervised measures are worthwhile (see page 13). But if significant improvements are noticed after the stricter diet then it is likely that your symptoms can be controlled or improved in the long term by careful avoidance of offending food. You should now proceed to stage 3, the reintroduction (page 19).

COPING WITH PROBLEMS ON THE EXCLUSION DIETS

YOUR WEIGHT Getting sufficient energy-rich foods is a problem on an exclusion diet. Many people experience weight loss due to large water and body fat losses at the start of the diet. Exclusion diets are not designed to be slimming diets. Therefore, if maintaining your weight is a problem, eat as much of the allowed foods as you like. Give yourself extra servings of rice and potatoes and top up with foods from the baking section later in the book. Each recipe gives an approximate energy value in kilocalories and kilojoules allowing you, if you wish, to estimate your daily energy intake from the recipes.

If on the other hand you start on the diet overweight, or you begin to put on too much weight, then select those recipes with the lower energy values; avoid sugar and sugary foods and try not to fry your foods or use too much margarine on your special breads and biscuits.

LACK OF DIETARY FIBRE Also popularly known as roughage, dietary fibre is found only in plant foods. The best source is cereal foods but vegetables and fruit also contribute significant amounts to the diet. Fibre in the diet increases stool bulk, thereby alleviating constipation. You should have no problem maintaining a good fibre intake on our basic exclusion diet. But you will have to be more careful with the stricter exclusion diet since many of the cereal foods are omitted. Adults should aim, according to the latest medical reports, to have a daily intake of at least 30 g dietary fibre. To help achieve this, each recipe has an approximate fibre value. If necessary, increase your diet's fibre content by adding soya or rice bran.

If constipation becomes a problem, then you may need the extra help of a natural bulk laxative such as Normacol.

VITAMINS AND MINERALS Having as varied a diet as possible during the exclusion period should ensure that you receive an adequate supply of vitamins and minerals, considering that you will only be on this diet for a few weeks. If you wish to have a vitamin supplement when on the stricter exclusion diet, then take the recommended dose of Abidec vitamin drops.

Because you are excluding all milk products from your daily diet, we recommend that you take a calcium supplement, such as calcium lactate, even though some brands of soya milk contain added calcium.

Additive-free vitamin and calcium supplements are available without prescription.

STAGE 3: THE REINTRODUCTION

Your next task is to isolate the culprit foods by continuing to observe your symptoms as you reintroduce the excluded foods to your diet one by one. If you have not followed the basic or stricter exclusion diets but simply stopped eating all suspect foods (such as shellfish) you can confirm your allergy to them by the same process. Continue to keep your food diary.

As a general guide, test one new food per week for eczema and migraine. For all other food-allergic conditions you can introduce a new food every third day. When testing a new food you should eat it daily and in adequate amounts, as suggested below. Any food that does not upset you can then be kept in your diet and eaten as desired.

Ensure that you eat only the food you are supposed to be testing – many foods are made up of more than one ingredient, for instance, white bread will have had its flour bleached by a chemical; it also contains yeast (important to note if you are reintroducing foods after the stricter exclusion diet). It may contain preservatives (most ready-wrapped breads do), as well as milk, fats, egg and soya flour. Careful label-reading is of vital importance, as if you get a reaction from a composite food, you will not know which of the ingredients is to blame. Advice on how to test for preservatives and colourings is given below.

If you are unsure whether a food is causing a reaction, leave it out for now and test it again later. If a food causes you to have a reaction – stop eating it. There is no need to complete the testing period. Allow yourself time enough to recover before testing a new food.

Reintroduce excluded foods in whatever order suits you best. Most people start by testing the foods they missed most on the exclusion diet. Below are rough guidelines for reintroducing foods, together with suggestions on the quantities to eat.

QUANTITIES TO REINTRODUCE

WHEAT Test 3–4 slices wholemeal bread, homemade or bought fresh from a baker who can tell you what the ingredients are (Prewett's wrapped wholemeal bread would be suitable, but the oil used in its preparation is not always specified). Test for wheat allergy also with wholemeal flour in pastry, or as thickening in a sauce if you know you are not allergic to the other ingredients.

TEA Test with 4–5 cups of tea (without milk).

COWS' MILK AND BEEF Test with 600 ml/1 pint pasteurized milk and 75 g/3 oz fresh beef. If you react, test separately later. If you react to cows' milk then try goats' milk (many people who are sensitive to cows' milk also react to goats' milk).

EGG AND CHICKEN Test with 1 egg (boiled, poached, fried or scrambled) and 75 g/3 oz chicken. If you react, test separately later. Ducks' eggs can be tolerated by some people allergic to chickens' eggs, but they can carry harmful bacteria and are therefore a health hazard.

COFFEE Test with 4–5 cups of black coffee. If you react, test instant and coffee beans separately.

CITRUS FRUIT Test with 200 ml/⅓ pint fresh orange juice or with 2 fresh oranges.

FISH AND SHELLFISH Test with 100 g/4 oz fish. If you react, test separately later.

BERRY FRUITS Test with 75 g/3 oz mixed berry fruits. If you react, test separately later.

CHOCOLATE Test with 50 g/2 oz plain dark chocolate. If milk is back in your diet then you can test with milk chocolate. Cocoa can also be tried.

DAIRY PRODUCE If you reacted to milk, also test: cheese (white Cheddar type), yogurt (plain unsweetened) and colour-free butter.

NUTS Test with 50 g/2 oz mixed nuts, including peanuts, but not the dry-roasted type which contain preservatives. If you react, you may like to test the individual nuts later. Remember whole nuts should not be given to children under five years old, as they may be inhaled accidentally.

PRESERVATIVES Test by eating all the foods

you know don't cause a reaction but which are labelled as containing added preservatives – fizzy drinks, ham, bacon and most types of ready-wrapped bread, for example.

COLOURINGS Test by eating all the foods allowed but with added colourings, such as coloured sweets, jelly and fruit squashes.

ALCOHOL Test with white wine first.

Reintroducing foods excluded on the stricter exclusion diet:

TAP WATER Test by cooking with it and drinking water.

POTATOES Test by eating 100 g/4 oz potatoes in whichever form preferred.

YEAST Test by taking 3 brewer's yeast tablets or 2 teaspoons baker's yeast.

OATS Test by eating 50 g/2 oz oats made into porridge or biscuits.

BARLEY Test by eating 2–3 tablespoons of either barley flakes for breakfast or of pearl barley added to soups and stews.

RYE Test by eating 3–4 rye crispbreads,

Original Ryvita, for example, and by using rye flour in baking and cooking.

CORN Test by eating corn on the cob, homemade popcorn and maize flour for cooking.

You may have completed the reintroduction stage without finding a single food that provokes your symptoms. If your symptoms return at a later date, you should go on our exclusion diet(s) again, but not until you have been eating your normal daily diet for at least six months. If after a second trial you still can't isolate culprit foods and symptoms persist, the likelihood is that food is not the cause of your symptoms.

If you have found foods that do affect you, then test these foods again. This is to rule out any coincidental and therefore misleading conclusions.

STAGE 4: LIVING ON YOUR ALLERGY-FREE DIET

When you have excluded culprit foods and arrived at a diet that allows you to remain symptom-free or on which your symptoms are significantly improved, ask your doctor to refer you to a dietitian who will be able to check the nutritional adequacy of this diet. Remember that the more foods you need to avoid, the greater the risk that your diet will not be nutritionally sound.

If you have discovered that you are allergic to either wheat, cows' milk, eggs, colourings or preservatives, or a combination of these, you can use the appropriately coded recipes in this book on your allergy-free diet. See also our meal plan suggestions on pages 120–3.

You can test yourself periodically with the foods that you reacted to – perhaps twice a year – just in case you no longer react to that food. Some people find they are able to eat small quantities of an offending food without their symptoms returning. Others can tolerate the well-cooked form of the food they are allergic to. Evaporated milk, for example, which is heat treated at a much higher temperature than pasteurized milk, is tolerated by some people who are sensitive to milk.

SHOPPING FOR ALLERGY-FREE FOODS

Shopping, for people who have to exclude certain foods and additives from their diet, needs a good deal of investigative work.

In an increasing number of Western

countries the ingredients in most foods have to be listed by law, though in Britain you will not find a list of ingredients with unpacked goods, some small packaged goods or chocolate and cocoa products; nor need some ingredients be fully identified, for example, oils need only be described as vegetable or animal; cheese, fish, meat, nuts, herbs, spices and starch can also remain unspecified on the ingredients list.

If you can't find the information you require on the packaging, check with the manufacturer. If you are still in doubt as to whether a product is suitable for you, ask your dietitian. In the meantime, the safest policy is to leave it out of your diet.

HIDDEN INGREDIENTS

Some products contain ingredients, such as the margarine in biscuits, which are themselves made of two or more substances. In our experience these substances are not always disclosed on food labelling. Again, if in doubt try contacting the manufacturer or ask your dietitian for advice.

One of the biggest problems in interpreting food labelling regulations is that a food additive need not be identified unless it serves a specific function in the finished product. Most white flour used in bread making, for example, is treated with bleaching agents, but they are not disclosed on the ingredients list. It is for this reason that we suggest you use wholemeal bread during the reintroduction stage.

The best policy is always to buy fresh (or frozen) natural foods. Throughout the recipe section we have tried to use ingredients that are easily available, but for some of the products you will have to find a reputable wholefood or health food shop.

In our recipes certain brand-name foods are mentioned. This is because we have checked the ingredients with the manufacturers. However, manufacturers can change their formulas and it is sensible to look at the ingredients list every time you buy something. Unless you are sure what a particular food contains, it is best avoided.

If you wish to substitute other brand-name foods for any reason, check the labelling carefully, and, as always, if in doubt contact the manufacturer for further information, or seek your dietitian's advice to ensure that it does not contain any forbidden ingredients.

For detailed information on additives see page 124.

MEDICINES

Medications need not have all their contents declared – there may be colourings in the pill coating, for example. It is wise to remind your doctor of any foods you are avoiding when being prescribed medicines.

You could also try asking your pharmacist to check the contents of any medicine you are unsure about. Hospital pharmacies are usually very good at providing a drug information service.

COMMON FORBIDDEN FOODS AND THEIR ALTERNATIVES

The purpose of this section is to alert you to the foods that are derived from or which may contain forbidden foods, and to suggest alternatives to them.

MILK

The following foods and ingredients are derivatives of milk and should be avoided if you are allergic to it: lactose, butter, yogurt, skimmed milk powder, non-fat milk solids, cream, caseinates, casein, whey, lactalbumin, cheese.

For babies and young children, only the soya baby milk formulas such as Cow and Gate Formula S and Wysoy are to be used. There are other suitable baby milks available, but ask your doctor or dietitian which are recommended.

For older children and adults the soya milks, Plamil, Itona and Granose, may be used as a replacement for milk, and if you are cutting out all milk products, we recommend that you take calcium supplements, even though some brands of soya milk contain extra calcium. When a milk substitute is mentioned in the recipes, one of the soya milks may be used.

In some of the milk-free recipes, goats' milk yogurt is used. You should only include this in your diet if you know that you can tolerate it. Likewise, test whether you can tolerate goats' cheese. We do not recommend that goats' or ewes' milk are given to babies, as they are not nutritionally adequate. For older children and adults, if goats' or ewes' milk are not pasteurized, they should be boiled before use to destroy any harmful bacteria.

Tofu – made from soya beans – makes a good alternative to yogurt or soft cheese. Morinaga Tofu is used in our recipes.

Australian readers see page 123.

MARGARINES

Certain margarines can be used as alternatives to butter and some ordinary margarines, which also contain milk. These are:

TOMOR A hard margarine that contains rapeseed oil, palm oil, soya oil and a natural vegetable dye.

GRANOSE This is a softer margarine that contains soya oil, rapeseed oil, coconut oil and soya lecithin.

WHITE FLORA A hard fat for frying and pastry-making that contains sunflower oil, soya oil and rapeseed oil.

PREWETT'S SUNFLOWER MARGARINE A soft margarine that contains sunflower oil, soya oil and natural additives.

Australian readers see page 123.

COOKING AND SALAD OILS

Choose 100 per cent pure oils rather than a mixture of unknown oils. In the recipes we use corn oil, sunflower oil and olive oil. Whenever possible choose the oils and margarines that are labelled 'high in polyunsaturates', as these are better for your health.

BEEF

If beef provokes a reaction, you will also need to exclude suet and gelatine. An alternative to gelatine is Gelozone, a vegetable product containing natural ingredients. Agar agar and Carragena are alternatives to gelatine available in Australia.

EGGS

The following are egg derivatives: egg yolk, egg white, albumen, ovalbumin and lecithin (but not vegetable lecithin).

An allergy-free alternative to egg is Ener-G egg replacer which contains potato and tapioca starch and methyl cellulose and is available from some health food shops and by mail order from the manufacturer G.F. Dietary Supplies Ltd (see page 125).

If you wish to use another brand of egg replacer you must ensure it is totally egg-free, as many egg substitute products are actually based on egg and its derivatives.

Our recipes have been tested with Ener-G. If you are using an alternative brand, it might be wise, when using it for the first time, to experiment with a recipe for which success is not essential. You should not have any problems, though, if you follow the manufacturer's instructions.

Australian readers see page 123.

WHEAT

The following should also be avoided if you are allergic to wheat: wheat starch, edible starch, semolina, modified starch, cereal filler, cereal binder, rusks, flour, farina and hydrolysed vegetable proteins (HVP). HVP can also be made from soya. Remember that gluten-free products need not necessarily be wheat-free. Don't assume that rye bread is made from 100 per cent rye flour – it mostly contains some wheat flour. Alternatives to wheat are listed below; unless stated to the contrary all are gluten-free.

SAGO Bland tasting, but good for milk puddings and can be mixed with other flours for biscuit making.

BROWN RICE AND BROWN RICE FLOUR We prefer this to the white rice products because of its higher fibre, vitamin and mineral content. Rice flour biscuits and cakes turn out rather crumbly due to its poor binding properties, but if you add grated apple or quince it will help to bind the mixture. Rice noodles made from rice only are available from Chinese food shops.

RYE FLOUR This has some gluten and therefore is useful for making bread. It needs mixing with other flours, otherwise the final product tends to be rather heavy.

BARLEY FLOUR AND FLAKES Malt is made from barley. Like rye, it contains some gluten and you can use it to make bread.

OATMEAL AND OAT FLAKES These contain a little gluten, but some coeliacs are allowed them in their diet. They are very useful for making biscuits and as a binder for homemade sausages and meat loaves.

MAIZE FLOUR (CORN) Yellow in colour, this is made from ground corn-on-the-cob kernels. Traditionally it is used to make polenta and tortillas. Mixed with other flours, it can be used in biscuits and cakes.

SOYA FLOUR This is another yellow flour, but made from the soya bean. It has a slightly musty smell and taste, and is best blended with other flours. Store it wrapped, in the fridge. Soya flour is an excellent source of protein and vitamins for people on vegetarian diets.

BUCKWHEAT FLOUR Not related to wheat at all, this comes from the same family as rhubarb. It has a rather distinctive flavour and good binding properties, which make it useful in baking. Buckwheat pasta can be made or bought.

POTATO FLOUR This is not instant mashed potato. The flour is fine and white without much taste. It is a useful thickening agent for soups and gravies and combines well with other flours for baking.

GRAM FLOUR Made from ground chickpeas, this is widely used in Indian cooking. Like soya flour, it is a good source of protein, vitamins and minerals for vegetarians.

MILLET FLOUR AND FLAKES These make good biscuits and the flakes can be used as a base for muesli.

CAROB POWDER This is a useful binder in baking because of its pectin content. It is ideal as an alternative to chocolate or cocoa for drinks or in baking.

BABIES AND INFANTS

In this section we suggest ways of dealing with the problems of feeding a potentially allergic infant. We are not, however, aiming to provide a comprehensive baby feeding guide.

Childhood allergies are common. One in five children will suffer from an allergic condition at some time. If there is no history of allergies in the family a child still has a 5 per cent chance of developing an allergy; this rises to 30 per cent if one parent has an allergic condition (such as eczema, asthma or hay fever) and to 60 per cent if both parents are affected. These facts need to be considered when deciding how your child should be fed from birth and later weaned.

BREAST FEEDING

In the light of recent scientific research we recommend exclusive breast feeding, on demand, for the first six months. Exclusive breast feeding until six months is almost always adequate and mother's milk contains all the necessary nutrients.

Weigh your baby regularly. If he or she is gaining weight consistently and is obviously alert and healthy, then there is no need for extras before the age of six months. But if your baby is no longer gaining weight satisfactorily, or loses weight, this may indicate problems with breast feeding, and you should consult your health visitor or doctor.

See page 125 for suggestions on where to obtain further advice on breast feeding.

WEANING

The following advice is for weaning the allergic or at-risk baby. If your baby shows no signs of allergy, and there is no history of allergies in the immediate family, there is no need to be too concerned about the order in which solids are introduced. But for the at-risk baby, it seems logical to introduce first the foods that least often cause allergic reactions and to delay the introduction of common allergy-provoking foods such as cows' milk, eggs, wheat, citrus fruits, nuts, chocolate, fish, colourings and preservatives.

FROM SIX MONTHS

As solids will be introduced very gradually to the at-risk baby, it may be wise to supplement the diet with the recommended doses of additive-free preparations such as Abidec, for vitamins, and Niferex, for iron until 12 months of age.

Introduce only one new food group at a time, such as cereals or fruit, giving it daily for one week. Initially your baby may only take teaspoon amounts of the new food. Watch for adverse reactions (red itchy skin rash; very loose, watery, offensive stools; or more dramatic rapid reactions such as swelling and redness of lips and face). If any of these occur then abandon that food and try it again in three or six months time. If symptoms persist after withdrawing the food, consult your doctor.

WHEN TO INTRODUCE SOLIDS

Below is a suggested order for the introduction of solids, which will give your baby one new food group per week (not one food per week). Those foods tolerated can then remain in your baby's diet but need not be given daily. See also our recipes for first solid foods on pages 99–100.

CEREALS (SIX MONTHS) Start with milk-free baby rice, mixed with water or expressed milk. Other cereals such as oats, barley, rye, millet can be introduced from seven months; wheat not until eight months.

ROOT VEGETABLES (SIX MONTHS) Potatoes, carrots, swede, turnip, parsnip.

FRUIT (SIX MONTHS) First try pears, bananas, apricots, apples, then the others. Citrus fruits and their juices should not be given until nine to ten months.

OTHER VEGETABLES (SEVEN MONTHS) First try marrow, cauliflower, broccoli and related vegetables. Then try peas, beans, lentils and tomatoes.

MEAT (SEVEN TO EIGHT MONTHS) First try lamb and turkey, then the others, leaving beef and chicken until last.

FISH (10 TO 11 MONTHS) First try white-fleshed fish such as cod, coley and plaice.

MILK Ideally three to four breastfeeds should be given until the age of 10 months. But if it proves impossible partially to breast feed your baby for this long, a baby formula milk will be needed to maintain adequate nourishment. A soya baby formula may be marginally better than a cows' milk formula, although allergies can develop to either.

After 10 months, cows' milk and other dairy products can be tried. Start with plain unsweetened yogurt, and if this causes no adverse reactions, try cows' milk in cooking, then as a drink. Last, try cheese.

If your baby does become allergic to both soya and cows' milk there are hypo-allergenic formulas on prescription, such as Nutramigen and Pregestimil.

Never give babies or small children ordinary soya milks since they are not nutritionally adequate. Nor are goats' or ewes' milk recommended for babies.

If in doubt get help from your health visitor or doctor – they can put you in touch with the community dietitian.

EGGS (ONE YEAR) Start with eggs in cooking, then as boiled eggs.

NUTS AND CHOCOLATE (TWO YEARS) Whole nuts must not be given to a child under five years because of the risk that they will be inhaled.

THE RECIPES

Each recipe in this book has a symbol which shows at a glance which diets it can be included in. Only select those recipes marked as suitable for your particular diet. All the recipes are free from artificial colourings, preservatives and flavourings.

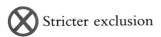 Stricter exclusion

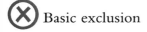 Basic exclusion

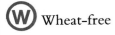 Wheat-free

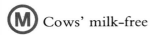 Cows' milk-free

 Egg-free

Ⓖ Gluten-free

All the recipes, except for the children's section, have an approximate energy and fibre value per serving or for the total recipe, whichever is the more appropriate. The energy values have been given in both kilocalories (kcal) and kilojoules (kJ).

When negligible fibre value is shown, it means that there is less than 1 g fibre in the serving size.

Measurements are given in both metric and imperial units. Use whichever system you are familiar with, but don't mix the two as the equivalents are not exact. When spoonfuls are mentioned use level spoons:

1 teaspoon = 5 ml
1 tablespoon = 15 ml.

Australian readers who use a 20 ml tablespoon should use 3 × 5 ml teaspoons to get the correct measure for the recipes.

Breakfast Recipes

Breakfast is a most important meal and one that should not be skipped. It may be that you are fortunate and are not allergic to a traditional breakfast based on egg, milk, cereals and toast – but if you are, then you will need alternative breakfast menu ideas. If you have been used to a cooked breakfast then there is no reason why a selection of allowed meats, fish, vegetables or fruits should not be eaten. You could try cold sliced meat served with slices of pineapple and potato cakes (page 31).

The muesli–type breakfast cereals are good and crunchy eaten dry or served with soya milk or a permitted fruit juice.

For the wheat-free and exclusion diets, include extras such as rice cakes, rye crispbreads or toast made from one of our special bread recipes and topped with Heinz baked beans, grilled tomatoes or mushrooms or jams of allowed fruits.

Fresh fruit always makes a healthy start to the day and can be varied according to the season.

OATY MUESLI

225 g/8 oz jumbo or rolled oats
100 g/4 oz barley or rye flakes
50 g/2 oz sesame seeds
50 g/2 oz sunflower seeds
100 g/4 oz seedless raisins or sultanas
25 g/1 oz pumpkin seeds
225 g/8 oz mixed dried fruit (apricots, peaches, figs, pears, dates, nectarines), chopped

SERVES 10
Per serving: **Energy** 250 kcal/1045 kJ
Fibre 6 g

Combine all the ingredients and store in an airtight container. Use as needed, and see Honeyed cereal (page 28) for serving suggestions and variation.

If you keep a vanilla pod in the container with the muesli it will be delicately and naturally flavoured.

PORRIDGE

BASIC RECIPE
50 g / 2 oz rolled oats
300 ml / ½ pint water
salt or sugar to taste

SERVES 2
Per serving: **Energy** 100 kcal/420 kJ
Fibre 1 g

Stir the oats and water together in a pan. Bring to the boil and simmer for 5 minutes, stirring occasionally. Add salt or sugar if used. Serve hot with milk substitute or milk if allowed.

VARIATIONS
MUESLI PORRIDGE Make the basic porridge recipe (above), and add 50 g/2 oz chopped mixed dried fruit (raisins, sultanas, apricots, dates, figs). Serve topped with 2–3 teaspoons desiccated coconut.

SERVES 2
Per serving: **Energy** 190 kcal/795 kJ
Fibre 4 g

PINEAPPLE PORRIDGE Make the basic porridge recipe (above), and add 100 g/4 oz roughly chopped fresh pineapple or tinned pineapple in natural juice. Serve each topped with 1 teaspoon finely chopped pineapple.

SERVES 3
Per serving: **Energy** 120 kcal/500 kJ
Fibre 2 g

MINTED PORRIDGE Make the basic porridge recipe (above), and add 2 tablespoons finely chopped mint and 2–3 teaspoons honey. Serve topped with sprigs of mint.

SERVES 2
Per serving: **Energy** 115 kcal/480 kJ
Fibre 2 g

RICE MUESLI

100 g / 4 oz brown rice, cooked
50 g / 2 oz millet flakes
25 g / 1 oz sunflower seeds
50 g / 2 oz seedless raisins or sultanas
100 g / 4 oz mixed dried fruit or fresh fruit
   (apricots, figs, pears, dates), chopped
25 g / 1 oz desiccated or fresh grated coconut

SERVES 4
Per serving: **Energy** 195 kcal/815 kJ
Fibre 4 g

Combine all the ingredients, or as many of them as you like. The muesli can be stored in the refrigerator for 2–3 days.

For serving suggestions and more variations, see Honeyed cereal (page 28).

VARIATION
Allowed commercially packaged breakfast cereals may be included instead of the millet flakes.

HONEYED CEREAL

4 tablespoons sunflower or safflower oil
225 g/8 oz clear honey
225 g/8 oz millet, rye or barley flakes
225 g/8 oz rolled oats
50 g/2 oz sesame seeds
50 g/2 oz dried peaches, pears or figs, chopped
100 g/4 oz sultanas or seedless raisins
50 g/2 oz pumpkin seeds

SERVES 12
Per serving: **Energy** 300 kcal/1255 kJ
                Fibre   3 g

Preheat the oven to moderate (180°C, 350°F, Gas Mark 4).

Warm the oil in a roasting tin. Stir in the honey, flakes and oats. Add the sesame seeds and cook in the oven for 20 minutes. Stir the mixture occasionally so that it browns evenly.

Remove from the oven. Allow to cool, then mix in the dried fruit and pumpkin seeds. Store in an airtight container.

Serve with milk or milk substitute, yogurt, fresh fruit or fruit juice, as your diet allows.

You can also use this mixture as a delicious filling for baked apples. If a vanilla pod is kept in the container, it will give the cereal a delicate vanilla flavour.

VARIATION
Add nuts if your diet allows.

SPICED FRUIT COMPÔTE

450 g/1 lb mixed dried fruit (apples, apricots, figs, peaches, pears, prunes, sultanas, etc.)
300 ml/½ pint apple juice
300 ml/½ pint water
1 cinnamon stick
2 cloves

SERVES 6
Per serving: **Energy** 175 kcal/730 kJ
                Fibre   9 g

Put the dried fruit in a bowl and pour over the apple juice and water. Add the spices and leave to soak overnight. Alternatively, pour over boiling juice and water and soak for a few hours.

Transfer to a pan and bring to the boil. Lower the heat, cover and simmer for about 20 minutes or until the fruit is tender, adding more water if the syrup becomes absorbed.

Serve with Rice custard (page 118).

STRAWBERRY AND MELON CUP

1 small Honeydew or Ogen melon, seeds
    removed
100 g/4 oz strawberries, hulled and sliced
5 cm/2 inch piece cucumber, sliced and quartered
finely grated rind and juice of 1 large orange
2 tablespoons chopped mint
15 g/½ oz split blanched pistachio nuts or
    roasted almonds
TO GARNISH
4–6 mint sprigs

SERVES 2
Per serving: **Energy** 100 kcal/420 kJ
                  Fibre 2 g

Cut the melon flesh into 1 cm/½ inch cubes or scoop into balls. Reserve the shells. Place in a bowl with the strawberries and cucumber.

Mix the orange rind and juice with the mint and nuts. Fold gently into the salad.

Spoon the salad back into the melon shells, pouring in any orange juice from the bowl. Serve chilled, garnished with sprigs of mint. This also makes a refreshing starter to a meal.

STRAWBERRY AND MELON CUP

REFRESHING FRUIT SALAD

1 mango, peeled and sliced
2 apples, cored and sliced
2 pears, peeled, cored and chopped
100 g / 4 oz seedless grapes
50 g / 2 oz blackcurrants
100 g / 4 oz watermelon, peeled, seeded and
    cubed
½ teaspoon vitamin C powder
150 ml / ¼ pint apple juice

TO GARNISH
chopped mint (optional)

SERVES 6
Per serving: **Energy** 50 kcal / 210 kJ
                 Fibre 2 g

Mix all the fruit together in a serving dish. Dissolve the vitamin C powder in the apple juice and pour it over the fruit. Scatter with mint leaves and serve on its own, or with Muesli (pages 26, 27) or yogurt if your diet allows.

This salad should be eaten straight away to get the maximum benefit from the high vitamin C content of the fresh fruit included in it.

VARIATION
Include any fresh fruit in season that your diet allows, such as peaches, cherries, blackberries, strawberries, redcurrants, kiwi, apricots or plums.

BANANA SHAKE

2 bananas
600 ml / 1 pint milk substitute
1 tablespoon clear honey, or to taste

SERVES 2
Per serving: **Energy** 235 kcal / 985 kJ
                 Fibre 5 g

Peel the bananas, then cut them into small pieces. Work to a purée with the milk and honey in an electric blender for 30 seconds.
Pour into chilled glasses to serve.

VARIATION
Make this shake with other fruit according to taste.

BREAKFAST SQUEAK

450 g / 1 lb potatoes, peeled, boiled and mashed
450 g / 1 lb cabbage, shredded and cooked
1 × 275 g (10 oz) can haricot beans, drained
salt and freshly ground black pepper
25 g / 1 oz special margarine
2 tablespoons sunflower oil

SERVES 6
Per serving: **Energy** 180 kcal / 755 kJ
                 Fibre 6 g

Mix together the potatoes, cabbage and beans. Beat in salt and pepper to taste and the margarine. Heat the oil in a large frying pan and turn the mixture into it. Cook until the base is golden. Serve hot.

VARIATION
Serve with Tomato sauce II (page 116).

TOFU FRUIT YOGURT

450 g / 1 lb tofu
1 large mango, peeled and sliced
1 × 400 g (14 oz) can pineapple with natural juice
3 teaspoons honey
vanilla essence (optional) to taste

SERVES 4
Per serving: **Energy** 145 kcal/605 kJ
Fibre 1 g

Put all the ingredients in a blender or food processor and blend until smooth. Chill and serve.

Make a yogurt drink by adding extra water or fruit juice.

VARIATION
Vary the choice of fruit to taste. Prunes, peaches, apples, apricots and bananas are all suitable alternatives.

POTATO CAKES

450 g / 1 lb cooked floury potatoes
pinch salt
50 g / 2 oz special margarine
about 4 tablespoons cornflour or rice flour
corn oil for cooking

MAKES 10 cakes
Each: **Energy** 110 kcal/460 kJ
Fibre negligible

Drain the cooked potatoes well and cover with a teacloth until dry and floury. Sieve into a mixing bowl with the salt. Beat in the margarine. Work in sufficient flour to make a soft dough that is easy to handle. Turn on to a floured board and roll or pat out 10 cakes 2 cm/¾ inch thick.

Cook in a lightly oiled frying pan until golden brown underneath. Turn and cook the other side. Serve hot, spread with extra margarine if liked, and honey or permitted jams (page 17).

SKINLESS SAUSAGES

225 g / 8 oz belly pork, rind removed, finely minced
100 g / 4 oz lean pork meat, finely minced
50 g / 2 oz fresh special breadcrumbs, moistened with a little water
¼–½ teaspoon mixed dried herbs
salt and freshly ground black pepper

MAKES 8 sausages
Each: **Energy** 140 kcal/585 kJ
Fibre negligible

Put all the ingredients in a large mixing bowl and mix thoroughly. Divide the mixture into 8 portions and roll into sausage shapes.

Grill the sausages for about 10–15 minutes, depending on the thickness.

Served with home-made Tomato sauce (page 116), they also make delicious teatime treats for children.

These sausages contain no preservatives or chemical additives, so they should be kept in the refrigerator and eaten within 2–3 days.

Soups
& Starters

Homemade soup is welcome any time. You can prepare soups in a variety of ways: thick and sustaining like Spicy lentil soup or lighter and refreshing like those based on vegetable purées, such as Spinach soup.

Many of the recipes in this section can be turned into a light lunch or supper by serving with bread – whether normal or special – and a side salad.

SPICY LENTIL SOUP

450 g / 1 lb red lentils
50 g / 2 oz special margarine
2 medium onions, peeled and chopped
2 cloves garlic, peeled and chopped
2 celery sticks, chopped
1 × 400 g (14 oz) can tomatoes, drained
1 chilli, seeded and chopped (optional)
1 teaspoon paprika
1 teaspoon chilli powder
1 teaspoon ground cumin

salt and freshly ground black pepper
1.2 litres / 2 pints Vegetable stock (page 115) or
   water

SERVES 8
Per serving: **Energy** 245 kcal / 1025 kJ
                  Fibre   7 g

Place the lentils in a bowl of water, picking out any discoloured ones or stones. Meanwhile, melt the margarine in a large saucepan over a low heat and gently fry the onions, garlic and celery until softened.

Drain the lentils and add them to the vegetables with the tomatoes. Mix well. Add the remaining ingredients, cover and simmer gently for about 2 hours. Add a little more water if the soup gets too thick and be careful not to burn the bottom.

Served hot this soup is a meal in itself.

VARIATION
Add any leftover meat that is allowed, such as turkey or lamb.

POTATO AND LEEK SOUP

25 g / 1 oz special margarine
450 g / 1 lb leeks, washed and sliced
450 g / 1 lb potatoes, peeled and sliced
1 large onion, peeled and sliced
600 ml / 1 pint water
salt and freshly ground black pepper
1 teaspoon grated nutmeg
1 bay leaf
300 ml / ½ pint milk substitute

TO GARNISH
½ teaspoon paprika or the green part of the leek
   cut in 5 cm / 2 inch julienne strips

SERVES 4
Per serving: **Energy** 215 kcal / 900 kJ
                  Fibre   5 g

Heat the margarine in a large saucepan. Add the leek, potato and onion and cook gently, covered, for about 5 minutes. Shake the pan occasionally to prevent the vegetables from sticking. Add the water, salt and pepper to taste, grated nutmeg and bay leaf. Liquidize in an electric blender or pass through a sieve.

Return the soup to the saucepan, add the milk substitute and reheat. Taste and adjust the seasoning. Sprinkle with a little paprika, if used, or add the leek julienne before serving the soup.

GAZPACHO

450 g / 1 lb tomatoes, skinned, seeded and
    chopped
2 garlic cloves, chopped
3 tablespoons olive oil
2 tablespoons wine or cider vinegar
600 ml / 1 pint water
½ teaspoon sugar
½ cucumber, peeled and roughly chopped
salt and freshly ground black pepper
TO GARNISH
½ cucumber, diced

1 small onion, peeled and chopped
1 small green pepper, cored, seeded and diced
croûtons made with special bread

SERVES 6
Per serving: **Energy** 75 kcal / 315 kJ
              Fibre 1 g

Put the tomatoes in a blender or food processor with the garlic, olive oil, vinegar, water, sugar and cucumber. Add salt and pepper to taste. Blend on maximum for 30 seconds or until smooth.

Pour the gazpacho into a soup tureen and chill in the refrigerator for at least 2 hours.

Dice the cucumber and place in a small serving bowl. Place the chopped onion, green pepper and croûtons in other small bowls. Serve the gazpacho with the vegetable accompaniments and croûtons.

SHRIMP AND CUCUMBER SOUP

1 large cucumber, peeled
15 g / ½ oz special margarine
1 garlic clove, peeled
½ onion, peeled and chopped
1 teaspoon cornflour or potato flour
1 litre / 1¾ pints allowed Meat stock (page 114)
1 sprig dill, chopped
50 ml / 2 fl oz dry cider (optional)
100 g / 4 oz peeled shrimps

salt and freshly ground black pepper
pinch sugar

SERVES 6
Per serving: **Energy** 65 kcal / 270 kJ
              Fibre negligible

Halve the cucumber lengthwise, scoop out the seeds and discard. Chop the cucumber flesh into small pieces.

Melt the margarine in a pan, add the garlic and fry until golden brown. Remove and discard the garlic. Add the onion and cucumber to the pan and cook for 2–3 minutes.

Combine the flour with a little of the stock, then add to the remaining stock. Add the thickened stock and half the dill to the pan and cook, stirring until the soup starts to boil. Reduce the heat and simmer the soup gently for about 25 minutes.

Remove half of the cucumber from the soup with a slotted spoon and purée in a blender or food processor until smooth. Return the purée to the soup and stir well to blend. Add the cider, if used, and shrimps and cook gently for about 5 minutes. Season with salt and pepper to taste and add the sugar.

Transfer to warmed individual soup bowls and sprinkle with the remaining dill to serve.

FROM THE TOP: RICE AND TOMATO SOUP;
SHRIMP AND CUCUMBER SOUP; GAZPACHO

RICE AND TOMATO SOUP

4 tablespoons olive oil
2 garlic cloves, peeled and halved
1 onion, peeled and chopped
750 g / 1½ lb tomatoes, skinned and chopped
1 litre / 1¾ pints allowed Meat stock (page 114)
2 tablespoons long-grain rice
1 sprig basil, chopped
salt and freshly ground black pepper
TO GARNISH
basil leaves

SERVES 6
Per serving: **Energy** 140 kcal / 585 kJ
Fibre 2 g

Heat the oil in a large pan, add the garlic and fry until golden brown. Remove and discard the garlic. Add the onion and tomatoes to the pan and fry for 2–3 minutes, stirring frequently.

Add the stock, rice and chopped basil and simmer, over a low heat, for about 20 minutes. Season to taste with salt and black pepper.

Transfer to a warmed soup tureen and garnish with basil leaves to serve.

SPINACH SOUP

25 g/1 oz special margarine
450 g/1 lb spinach with stalks, washed
1 small onion, peeled and chopped
1 dessert apple, cored, peeled and sliced
1 small potato, chopped
600 ml/1 pint Vegetable stock (page 115) or
    water
½ teaspoon grated nutmeg
salt and freshly ground black pepper

SERVES 4
Per serving: **Energy** 120 kcal/500 kJ
                 Fibre 7 g

Melt the margarine in a large saucepan over a low heat and add the wet spinach. Cook over a moderate heat, turning constantly, until the spinach is reduced in size and partially cooked. Roughly chop the spinach in the saucepan and add the remaining ingredients. Simmer for about 45 minutes.

Allow the soup to cool slightly, then transfer to a food processor or blender and process for about 1 minute, until smooth. Alternatively, press the soup through a sieve. Serve hot or cold.

SCOTCH BROTH

450 g/1 lb middle neck of lamb
1.2 litres/2 pints water
50 g/2 oz pearl barley
salt and freshly ground black pepper
2 onions, peeled and finely chopped
4 carrots, peeled and finely chopped
2 medium turnips, peeled and finely chopped
2 leeks, cleaned and thinly sliced
25 g/1 oz rice or soya bran (optional)

TO GARNISH
chopped fresh parsley

SERVES 4
Per serving: **Energy** 300 kcal/1255 kJ
                 Fibre 6 g

Place the meat in a saucepan with the water, bring to the boil and skim. Add the barley and seasoning to taste, cover and cook gently for 30 minutes, then add the vegetables and bran. Continue cooking for a further 1½ hours.

Lift out the lamb, remove the meat from the bone and cut into small pieces. Return the meat to the pan. Add more liquid and reheat if required. Garnish with parsley.

NOODLES WITH GARLIC SAUCE

225 g/8 oz buckwheat noodles (page 49) or
    bought buckwheat spaghetti
GARLIC SAUCE
3 tablespoons olive oil
1 small onion, peeled and finely chopped
1–2 garlic cloves, peeled and finely chopped
sea salt and freshly ground black pepper
chopped fresh parsley

SERVES 4
Per serving: **Energy** 295 kcal/1235 kJ
                 Fibre 1 g

Cook the noodles in boiling salted water until *al dente*. Drain thoroughly.

To make the sauce, heat the oil in a small saucepan, add the onion and garlic and fry until transparent. Pour over the freshly cooked pasta. Add salt and plenty of pepper and sprinkle generously with the chopped fresh parsley.

VARIATION
Serve with grated Parmesan cheese if your diet allows.

SALAD WITH FETA CHEESE

4 tomatoes, quartered
1 large cucumber, sliced
1 medium onion, peeled and thinly sliced (optional)
100 g/4 oz feta cheese, broken into chunks
12–16 black olives
4 tablespoons olive oil
DRESSING
2 tablespoons cider vinegar or lemon juice
1 garlic clove, peeled and chopped (optional)

salt and freshly ground black pepper
1 tablespoon finely chopped fresh basil and oregano

SERVES 4
Per serving: Energy 240 kcal/1005 kJ
Fibre 1 g

Place the tomatoes, cucumber, onion, cheese and olives in a bowl.

Combine the ingredients for the dressing in a screw top jar. Shake until the mixture is pale and smooth, then pour over the salad. Toss well and serve as a starter (serves 6) or as a lunch dish with special bread.

HUMMUS

225 g/8 oz dried chickpeas or 1 × 400 g (14 oz) can chickpeas
100 g/4 oz Tahini paste (bought or see page 116)
3 tablespoons olive oil
3 garlic cloves, peeled and crushed
grated rind and juice of 1 large lemon
salt and freshly ground black pepper

TO GARNISH
6 olives
1 tablespoon olive oil

SERVES 12
Per serving: Energy 145 kcal/605 kJ
Fibre 2 g

If using dried chickpeas, which have a very distinctive flavour, soak them overnight in plenty of cold water. Next day, drain the chickpeas and simmer gently in fresh water for 1½ hours, until tender, then drain. If using canned chickpeas for speed and convenience, simply drain them in a sieve.

Combine all the ingredients in a food processor or blender and process for 1 minute. Taste and correct the seasoning if necessary, then process again briefly.

Spoon into a serving bowl or on to individual plates and garnish with olives and a little olive oil. Serve with special bread.

This hummus can be frozen without the garnish.

VARIATION
For exclusion diets use 1 tablespoon finely chopped parsley instead of the lemon rind and juice.

GUACAMOLE

1 small hot green chilli
2 ripe avocados, peeled, halved and stoned
1 small onion, peeled and finely chopped
2 teaspoons chopped coriander leaves
½ teaspoon vitamin C powder mixed with 2
   teaspoons water
pinch salt

SERVES 4

Per serving: **Energy** 145 kcal/605 kJ
               Fibre   1 g

Pound the green chilli using a pestle and mortar. Mash the avocado flesh lightly in a bowl. Add the onion, ground chilli, coriander, vitamin C mixture (to help prevent browning) and salt to taste. Mix thoroughly.

Serve the Guacamole as a dip with Tortilla chips (page 87).

ARTICHOKE HEARTS WITH VINAIGRETTE

4 fresh artichokes
150 ml/5 fl oz Vinaigrette dressing (page 117)
TO GARNISH
12 black olives
1 tablespoon chopped parsley

SERVES 4
Per serving: **Energy** 215 kcal/900 kJ
Fibre negligible

Trim the artichokes and simmer for 20–25 minutes in lightly salted water. Drain, cool and pull out the inner core of leaves. Scrape out the choke with a teaspoon, and carefully remove the hearts.

Marinate the hearts in the Vinaigrette dressing for 15 minutes. Remove with a slotted spoon and serve in individual dishes, garnished with the olives and chopped parsley.

LES CRUDITÉS

VEGETABLES
Young courgettes, fennel, green and red peppers, spring onions, chicory, cucumber, small firm Brussels sprouts, red and green cabbage, carrots, celery, mushrooms, broccoli, cauliflower, endive, radishes, young turnips
FRUITS
Apples, pears, pineapple

DRESSINGS
Vinaigrette dressing (page 117)
Bagna cauda (page 118)
Ravigote dressing (page 117)
Yogurt dressing (page 117)

Prepare a selection of the above vegetables and fruits so they can be eaten with the fingers. Provide a choice of dressings and offer them as dips. (Check the relevant pages to find the diet symbols for the dressings.)

LES CRUDITÉS WITH VARIOUS DRESSINGS.
FROM THE TOP: VINAIGRETTE (P.117);
RAVIGOTE (P.117); BAGNA CAUDA (P.118)

VEGETABLES À LA GRÈCQUE

4 tablespoons olive oil
300 ml / ½ pint water
4 medium carrots, peeled
1 small cauliflower, quartered
4 small globe artichokes, stalks removed
4 small courgettes, trimmed
8 button mushrooms, wiped
1–2 garlic cloves, peeled
small bunch parsley
1 bay leaf
1 sprig thyme

salt and freshly ground black pepper
TO GARNISH
chopped parsley

SERVES 4
Per serving: **Energy** 150 kcal / 630 kJ
            Fibre 4 g

Put the oil and water into a large saucepan, add the vegetables, garlic, herbs and seasoning to taste and cook until just tender.

Remove from the liquid with a perforated spoon and arrange in a serving dish. Boil the liquid in the pan until reduced to 150 ml / ¼ pint. Strain over the vegetables.

Serve the vegetables cold sprinkled with chopped fresh parsley.

VARIATION
Replace the vegetables with 225 g / 8 oz button mushrooms, 2 large sliced onions, 225 g / 8 oz sliced leeks and 225 g / 8 oz peeled, quartered and seeded tomatoes.

CRAB SALAD WALDORF

1 × 750 g (1½ lb) crab, cooked and cooled
2 crisp dessert apples, peeled, cored and diced
1 celery stick, finely sliced
1 garlic clove, peeled and crushed
4 tablespoons Mayonnaise (page 118)
1 tablespoon snipped chives
1 tablespoon finely chopped parsley
salt and freshly ground black pepper
¼ teaspoon wheat-free French mustard
1 lettuce heart, rinsed and dried

TO GARNISH
parsley sprigs

SERVES 4
Per serving: **Energy** 225 kcal / 1065 kJ
            Fibre 1 g

Remove the crab meat from the shell, putting the white and brown meat in separate bowls. Combine the white crab meat with the apple, celery and garlic. Stir in the mayonnaise, chives and parsley and season with salt and pepper. Add the mustard and a few drops of vinegar to the brown crab meat and season to taste with salt and pepper.

Line 4 scallop shells or shallow individual dishes with the lettuce. Divide the white meat mixture equally between them, and top with the brown meat. Garnish with sprigs of parsley.

COURGETTE FLAN

175 g/6 oz Shortcrust pastry (page 87)
450 g/1 lb courgettes, trimmed
2 teaspoons egg replacer
300 ml/½ pint milk substitute
salt and freshly ground black pepper
grated nutmeg (optional)
1 garlic clove, peeled and crushed (optional)
1 teaspoon tomato purée
Tabasco sauce to taste

SERVES 4
Per serving: **Energy** 270 kcal/1130 kJ
                  Fibre 2 g

Preheat the oven to hot (200°C, 400°F, Gas Mark 6).

Roll out the pastry and use to line an 18 cm/7 inch flan tin. Line the pastry with greaseproof paper and weigh it down with dried beans. Bake blind for 15 minutes. Remove the paper and beans and bake for a further 5–10 minutes. Set aside to cool.

Slice the courgettes and blanch in boiling water for 1 minute, drain well and set aside. Blend the remaining ingredients in a food processor. Arrange the courgette slices in the pastry case. Pour in the blended mixture. Bake for 30–40 minutes or until set.

VARIATION
Use 2 eggs instead of the egg replacer if your diet allows.

POTTED PORK

100 g/4 oz pork back fat, cut into small pieces
450 g/1 lb boned pork (use equal quantities of lean and fatty pork)
2 tablespoons water
1 bouquet garni
salt and freshly ground black pepper
1 teaspoon ground mixed spice, or to taste

SERVES 8
Per serving: **Energy** 240 kcal/1005 kJ
                  Fibre negligible

Put the back fat in a heavy pan over a gentle heat for about 30 minutes until melted.

Meanwhile, cut the boned pork into small cubes, mixing the lean and fat meat together. Add the pork to the pan with the water, bouquet garni, salt, pepper to taste and spice.

Cover the pan and cook very gently for 4 hours, stirring occasionally. At the end of the cooking time the pork should have rendered down and become extremely soft.

Pour the meat and fat into small earthenware pots and leave to cool. The fat will rise to the surface of the pots and solidify, sealing the meat. Cover the pots with lids, then store in the refrigerator until needed. Serve with special toasted bread.

You can make Potted pork in larger quantities, as it keeps fresh for up to 2 months in the refrigerator.

VARIATION
Add 2–3 garlic cloves to the pan before cooking the pork.

Main Course Dishes

We have provided a variety of recipes here, some simple and adequate for everyday use and others best suited to more formal occasions.

The meat for most meat dishes is interchangeable (assuming it is permitted in your diet), as is the fish named in the fish recipes, and if a recipe specifies chicken you may use turkey instead, if preferred.

For a healthier diet, use as little fat as possible when cooking meat. Try also to reduce the amount of salt used, and experiment with fresh herbs and spices for extra flavour.

Keep leftovers and bones to make stock (page 114).

PORK IN HOT SAUCE

175 g/6 oz boned lean pork, shredded
2 spring onions, finely chopped
1 slice root ginger, finely chopped
1 garlic clove, finely chopped
1 tablespoon wheat-free soya sauce
1½ teaspoons cornflour
600 ml/1 pint corn oil for deep-frying
225 g/8 oz aubergine, cut into diamond-shaped chunks
1 tablespoon Tabasco

3–4 tablespoons stock (pages 114–5) or water
TO GARNISH
chopped spring onion

SERVES 2
Per serving: **Energy** 455 kcal/1905 kJ
Fibre 3 g

Put the pork in a bowl with the spring onions, ginger, garlic, soya sauce and cornflour. Mix well and leave to marinate for about 20 minutes.

Heat the oil in a wok or deep-fryer to 180°C/350°F. Lower the heat, add the aubergine and deep-fry for about 1½ minutes. Remove from the pan with a slotted spoon and drain on absorbent paper.

Pour off all but 1 tablespoon of oil from the pan, then add the pork and stir-fry for about 1 minute. Add the aubergine and Tabasco sauce and cook for about 1½ minutes. Moisten with the stock or water and simmer until the liquid has almost completely evaporated. Serve hot, garnished with chopped spring onion.

ABOVE: PORK IN HOT SAUCE; BELOW: STIR-FRIED SPINACH WITH LIVER (P.44)

STIR-FRIED SPINACH WITH LIVER

450 g/1 lb spinach, including stalks, washed
    and well drained
350 g/12 oz pig's liver, cut into thin triangular
    slices
2 tablespoons cornflour
4 tablespoons sunflower oil
2 slices root ginger
1 tablespoon wheat-free soy sauce

TO GARNISH
shredded spring onion

SERVES 3
Per serving: **Energy** 410 kcal/1715 kJ
            Fibre 9 g

Blanch the liver for a few seconds in boiling water, drain and coat with the cornflour.

Heat half the oil in a wok or frying pan. Add the spinach and stir-fry for 2 minutes. Remove from the pan, arrange around the edge of a serving dish and keep hot.

Heat the remaining oil in the pan until it reaches smoking point. Add the ginger, liver and soy sauce. Stir-fry for about 1 minute, until the liver is evenly browned, then tip over the spinach.

Serve immediately, garnished with shredded spring onion. *Illustrated on page 43.*

PORK WITH FENNEL

2 large fennel bulbs, trimmed and chopped
3 juniper berries, crushed
4 large pork chops, about 225 g/8 oz each,
    trimmed
salt and freshly ground black pepper
2 tablespoons olive oil

SERVES 4
Per serving: **Energy** 345 kcal/1445 kJ
            Fibre 1 g

Mix the fennel and juniper berries together and spread half the mixture in the base of a flat flameproof dish. Lay the pork chops on top, season to taste and sprinkle the remaining fennel mixture over the top. Spoon over the oil, cover and refrigerate for at least 4 hours, basting occasionally.

Heat the grill, uncover the dish and place the chops in the dish under the grill. Cook the chops for 10–12 minutes each side, turning them over frequently during cooking, until cooked through.

LAMB AND VEGETABLE CASSEROLE

225 g/8 oz lean cooked lamb, trimmed and
    cubed
75 g/3 oz leeks, sliced
100 g/4 oz cauliflower, broken into florets
50 g/2 oz mushrooms, sliced
75 g/3 oz carrots, peeled and sliced
2 tomatoes, sliced
salt and freshly ground black pepper
150 ml/¼ pint Meat stock (page 114)

SERVES 3
Per serving: **Energy** 230 kcal/960 kJ
            Fibre 3 g

Preheat the oven to moderate (180°C, 350°F, Gas Mark 4). Arrange the meat and vegetables in layers in a casserole. Season to taste. Pour over the stock and cover. Cook in the centre of the oven for 45 minutes.

VARIATION

Try this casserole with celeriac, fennel, courgettes and aubergine for a change.

LAMB ON SKEWERS

450 g / 1 lb boned leg or shoulder of lamb, trimmed and cut in cubes
3 small onions, peeled
1 garlic clove, peeled and crushed
salt
1 teaspoon ground ginger
Tabasco sauce
½ teaspoon ground turmeric
pinch ground coriander
1 large green pepper, cored, seeded and cut into 2.5 cm / 1 inch squares
8 mushrooms

4 small tomatoes
1 tablespoon sunflower oil
TO GARNISH
chopped mixed herbs

SERVES 4
Per serving: **Energy** 260 kcal / 1090 kJ
　　　　　　 Fibre 1 g

Put the lamb in a shallow dish. Grate one of the onions, mix it with the garlic, salt, ginger, a few drops of Tabasco, turmeric and coriander and pour over the lamb. Leave to marinate for 2 hours, stirring frequently.

Cut the remaining onions into quarters. Thread 4 kebab skewers with the lamb cubes, onion quarters, green pepper squares and mushrooms, alternating the ingredients until they are all used up. Thread a tomato at the end of each skewer, then brush the meat and vegetables with the oil.

Grill under a high heat for 12 minutes, turning the skewers frequently until the meat is cooked through. Sprinkle with herbs and serve on a bed of rice.

PORK STEAKS WITH OKRA

4 pork steaks, about 175 g / 6 oz each
1 tablespoon sunflower oil
2 tomatoes, skinned, quartered and seeded
2 teaspoons tomato purée
150 ml / ¼ pint water
100 g / 4 oz okra, stalk ends trimmed
salt and freshly ground black pepper
TO GARNISH
watercress sprigs

SERVES 4
Per serving: **Energy** 515 kcal / 2155 kJ
　　　　　　 Fibre 1 g

Wipe the pork steaks dry with absorbent kitchen paper. Heat the oil in a large frying pan, add the steaks and fry over a moderate heat until well browned on both sides. Remove the steaks from the pan with a slotted spoon and place overlapping in a warmed serving dish. Keep hot.

Add the remaining ingredients to the pan and cook for 8 minutes, stirring occasionally until the okra is just tender. Pour over the pork and serve garnished with watercress if liked. *Illustrated on page 46.*

VEAL WITH GRAPES

*2 large veal escalopes, about 225 g/8 oz each,
  halved crossways*
350 g/12 oz minced veal
2 tablespoons chopped parsley
2 tablespoons chopped tarragon
2 tablespoons snipped chives
salt and freshly ground black pepper
2 tablespoons olive oil
2 tablespoons cornflour or potato flour
300 ml/½ pint allowed Meat stock (page 114)

350 g/12 oz seedless green grapes
TO GARNISH
chopped tarragon

SERVES 4

Per serving:	**Energy**	310 kcal/1295 kJ
	Fibre	1 g

Beat the 4 pieces of veal between 2 sheets of cling film until very thin. Mix together the minced veal, herbs and seasoning, then divide between the veal pieces. Roll up and tie securely with thread or fine string.

Heat the oil in a large frying pan, add the veal parcels and fry over moderate heat until well browned on all sides. Remove from the pan with a slotted spoon and drain on absorbent kitchen paper.

Mix the flour with a little of the stock to form a smooth paste, then blend with the rest of the stock. Gradually stir the thickened stock into the pan with the meat juices and bring to the boil. Lower the heat, return the veal parcels to the pan, cover and simmer for 30 minutes. Add the grapes and simmer for a further 15 minutes.

To serve, remove the parcels from the sauce and cut off and discard the thread or string. Slice the veal neatly and arrange on a warmed serving plate. Pour over the sauce and garnish with tarragon, if liked.

VARIATION
For basic exclusion diet use turkey or pork instead of veal.

PORK OLIVIER WITH APPLE SAUCE

1.5 kg / 3–3½ lb piece loin of pork, kidney attached, rind removed and boned
salt and freshly ground black pepper
18 pimiento-stuffed green olives
TO GARNISH
1 bunch watercress
APPLE SAUCE
450 g / 1 lb cooking apples, peeled, cored and sliced
2–3 tablespoons water

SERVES 6
Per serving: **Energy** 660 kcal / 2760 kJ
Fibre 1 g

Preheat the oven to hot (200°C, 400°F, Gas Mark 6).

Open out the pork as flat as possible by cutting the fleshiest part diagonally. Sprinkle with salt and pepper. Skin, core and finely chop the kidney. Insert the kidney into one fold of the meat, the olives into the other. Roll up the meat and tie securely at regular intervals with thread or fine string. Weigh the pork and calculate the cooking time at 30 minutes per 450 g / 1 lb.

Put the pork in a small roasting tin and roast for the calculated cooking time. Allow to cool.

When cold, cut into thin slices, removing the thread or string, then arrange the slices on a bed of watercress.

To make the apple sauce, put the apples into a saucepan, add the water and simmer, covered, until soft – about 10 minutes. Purée in an electric blender or pass through a plastic sieve. Add a little sugar if the apples are very tart.

Serve the Pork olivier with the Apple sauce.

VARIATION
Gooseberry sauce is also a delicious accompaniment to Pork olivier. Use 225 g / ½ lb gooseberries in place of the apples.

FROM THE TOP: PORK STEAKS WITH OKRA (P.45); PORK OLIVIER WITH APPLE SAUCE; VEAL WITH GRAPES

LAMB WITH FRUIT

4 lamb chops, about 175 g/6 oz each, trimmed
1 teaspoon chopped fresh thyme
TOPPING
1½ tablespoons sunflower oil
1 onion, peeled and sliced
½ green pepper, cored, seeded and sliced
1 tablespoon potato flour
7 tablespoons Vegetable stock (page 115)
1 teaspoon vinegar
100 g/4 oz canned pineapple in natural juice,
    drained and chopped

2 teaspoons wheat-free soy sauce
freshly ground black pepper
TO GARNISH
fresh mint

SERVES 4
Per serving: **Energy** 205 kcal/860 kJ
                Fibre negligible

Preheat the oven to moderate (180°C, 350°F, Gas Mark 4).

Place each chop on a piece of foil and sprinkle with the thyme.

To make the topping, heat the oil in a saucepan and fry the onion and green pepper gently for 5 minutes, until soft. Mix the potato flour with a little of the vegetable stock to form a smooth paste. Blend this into the remaining stock then pour over the fried onion and green pepper. Add the remaining ingredients and bring to the boil, stirring. Cook for 2–3 minutes, then spoon on top of each chop.

Fold the foil over to make a parcel, seal and bake in the oven for 1 hour. Remove the foil and serve the chops garnished with mint.

VARIATION
Canned apricots, in natural juice, may be used instead of pineapple.

LAMB WITH POLENTA

2 tablespoons sunflower oil
450 g/1 lb lean boneless leg of lamb, trimmed
    and cut into 2.5 cm/1 inch cubes
1 × 400 g (14 oz) can tomatoes
150 ml/¼ pint water
1 sprig rosemary
1 sprig thyme
1 bay leaf
salt and freshly ground black pepper
100 g/4 oz mushrooms, sliced
1 green pepper, cored, seeded and sliced

Polenta (page 71)
TO GARNISH
chopped parsley

SERVES 4
Per serving: **Energy** 280 kcal/1170 kJ
                Fibre 1 g

Heat the oil in a flameproof casserole or heavy-based pan. Add the lamb and cook, stirring frequently, for 5 minutes or until evenly browned. Stir in the tomatoes with their juice and the water. Add the herbs and seasoning to taste. Stir well, then cover and simmer for 45 minutes.

Add the sliced mushrooms and green pepper to the casserole. Check the seasoning, cover and simmer the dish gently for a further 20 minutes.

Discard the herbs. Sprinkle with chopped parsley and serve with Polenta.

VARIATION
Can also be served with rice or pasta, if your diet allows.

STEAK WITH MANGETOUT

3 tablespoons sunflower oil
450 g / 1 lb mangetout peas
1 kg / 2 lb fillet or rump steak, cut into 4
1 teaspoon finely chopped fresh ginger
1 tablespoon wheat-free soy sauce
TO GARNISH
coriander leaves

SERVES 4
Per serving: **Energy** 335 kcal / 1400 kJ
Fibre 3 g

Heat 1 tablespoon of the oil in a pan. Add the mangetout and stir-fry for about 1 minute. Transfer to a serving plate and keep hot.

Add the remaining oil to the pan. When hot, add the steak and sear for 1 minute or until blood rises on the uncooked surface. Turn and sear the other side. Remove the steak and cut into 1 cm / ½ inch thick strips.

Return the steak to the pan with the ginger and soy sauce. Reduce the heat and continue cooking until the steak is cooked to your taste. Add it to the mangetout and garnish with coriander leaves to serve.

VARIATION
For exclusion diet use pork or turkey fillets instead of beef.

BUCKWHEAT NOODLES WITH MEAT SAUCE

MEAT SAUCE
1 small onion, peeled and chopped
3 tablespoons olive oil
2 tablespoons chopped celery
2 carrots, peeled and chopped
350 g / 12 oz lean minced beef or 175 g / 6 oz
minced beef and 175 g / 6 oz minced pork
salt and freshly ground black pepper
1 × 400 g (14 oz) can tomatoes, roughly
chopped, with their juice
pinch grated nutmeg (optional)
NOODLES
225 g / 8 oz buckwheat flour

pinch salt
2 teaspoons egg replacer mixed with 4
tablespoons water
1 tablespoon sunflower oil
4–5 tablespoons water

SERVES 4
Per serving: **Energy** 505 kcal / 2115 kJ
Fibre 3 g

For the meat sauce, gently fry the onion in the oil in a heavy-based saucepan until just translucent. Add the celery and carrot and cook for a further 2 minutes.

Add the meat, breaking it up with a fork. Season to taste and cook until the meat has browned.

Add the tomatoes and nutmeg, if used, and stir thoroughly. When the tomatoes start to bubble, turn the heat down and simmer, uncovered, for 2½–3 hours until cooked. If the sauce gets too dry add water.

For the noodles, put the flour, salt, egg replacer mixture and oil in a bowl. Mix

thoroughly, then add the water, a little at a time, to make a thick, fairly stiff dough. Alternatively, put all the ingredients in a food processor and blend until they come together to form a ball. Knead well.

Lightly flour the work surface and roll the dough out thinly. Cut into noodles.

Bring a large saucepan of lightly salted water to the boil. Add the noodles and boil for 3–5 minutes. Drain and serve immediately with the meat sauce.

The meat sauce can be made in large quantities and frozen, or stored in the refrigerator for up to 5 days.

CHINESE GRILLED FISH

6 thick pieces of white fish, about 175 g/6 oz
* each*
2 tablespoons wheat-free soy sauce
2 slices root ginger, peeled and chopped
¼ teaspoon 5-spice powder
2 tablespoons sunflower oil
pinch sugar
pinch pepper
1 tablespoon water
TO GARNISH
coriander sprigs
spring onion brushes

SERVES 6
Per serving: **Energy** 180 kcal/755 kJ
                    Fibre   negligible

Wipe over the fish and remove any visible scales or bones. Combine the remaining ingredients in a shallow dish. Place the fish in the dish and turn about to coat in the marinade. Leave for 1 hour, turning the fish once.

Line the grill pan with aluminium foil and lay the fish on it, skin side up. Pre-heat the grill. Pour over half the marinade and grill at high heat for 4–5 minutes. Pour over the remaining marinade and grill for a further 4–5 minutes.

Transfer to a warmed serving plate and pour over any remaining marinade. Garnish with coriander sprigs and spring onion brushes.

To make spring onion brushes, cut the leaves lengthwise almost to the base and stand in ice-cold water until they curl.

FISH WITH MACARONI

25 g/1 oz special margarine
1 garlic clove, peeled and crushed (optional)
2–3 celery sticks, washed and chopped
1 × 400 g (14 oz) can tomatoes, drained
300 ml/½ pint Fish or Vegetable stock (page 115)
100 g/4 oz short-cut, wheat-free macaroni
1 bay leaf
175 g/6 oz frozen sweetcorn
750 g/1½ lb coley, skinned and cut into chunks

salt and freshly ground black pepper
TO GARNISH
1 tablespoon chopped fresh parsley

SERVES 4
Per serving: **Energy** 275 kcal/1150 kJ
　　　　　　 Fibre 3 g

Melt the margarine in a large saucepan and lightly fry the garlic, if used, and celery. Add the tomatoes, stock, macaroni and bay leaf. Cover and simmer for 5–6 minutes. Add the sweetcorn and fish. Season and simmer gently for another 5–6 minutes, until the fish and pasta are tender.

　Serve hot, garnished with parsley.

BARBECUED MACKEREL WITH HONEY

2 large mackerel, about 450 g/1 lb each, cleaned and heads removed
2 tablespoons clear honey
1 carrot, peeled and cut in 5 cm/2 inch julienne strips
1 piece ginger root, peeled and shredded
freshly ground black pepper
1 tablespoon cider or wine vinegar
1 tablespoon wheat-free soy sauce

SERVES 4
Per serving: **Energy** 295 kcal/1235 kJ
　　　　　　 Fibre negligible

Place each mackerel on a greased piece of double aluminium foil large enough to enclose the whole fish. Spread each fish with honey.

　Divide the carrot, celery and ginger root between the fish. Add pepper to taste and sprinkle a little vinegar and soy sauce over each fish. Seal the edges of the foil well to form individual parcels. Place on the barbecue grill and cook over medium hot coals for about 20 minutes, turning once.

　The fish can also be baked in a preheated moderate oven (180°C, 350°F, Gas Mark 4) for 30 minutes.

TROUT WITH CAPERS

4 tablespoons sunflower oil
1 large garlic clove, peeled and crushed
75 g/3 oz capers, rinsed and lightly crushed
salt and freshly ground black pepper
4 × 175 g (6 oz) trout, cleaned and heads removed
2 tablespoons chopped fresh chives or parsley

SERVES 4
Per serving: **Energy** 355 kcal/1485 kJ
　　　　　　 Fibre 1 g

In a bowl, mix together the oil, garlic, capers and seasoning. Cover and leave for 1 hour to allow the flavours to blend.

Slash the fish 3 times diagonally on each side and arrange side by side on the grill rack. Spoon the dressing over the fish. Cook under a preheated, moderately hot grill for about 5 minutes each side, basting with the dressing from time to time. If necessary, increase the heat towards the end to brown and crisp the skin.

Transfer the fish to a warmed serving plate. Stir the chives or parsley into the pan juices, spoon over the trout and serve.

CARP WITH LEEK STUFFING

1 carp, weighing 1–1.25 kg/2–2½ lb, cleaned
salt and freshly ground white pepper
2–3 leeks
65 g/2½ oz special margarine
2 teaspoons mixed chopped fresh herbs (chives, parsley, thyme)
pinch ground allspice

SERVES 4
Per serving: Energy 240 kcal/1005 kJ
Fibre negligible

Soak the carp in lightly salted water for 3–4 hours. Rinse thoroughly and dry on absorbent kitchen paper. Season inside and out.

Trim the leeks and discard the green part. Slice the white, rinse and drain thoroughly. Melt half the margarine in a frying pan, add the leeks and herbs and cook for 2–3 minutes. Season to taste with salt and allspice. Allow to cool slightly.

Stuff the carp with the leek mixture and place in a greased ovenproof dish. Melt the remaining margarine and brush over the fish. Cook in a preheated moderate oven (180°C, 350°F, Gas Mark 4) for about 40 minutes, turning the fish over twice during the cooking time. Serve from the baking dish.

SOLE WITH PINEAPPLE AND POTATOES

4–8 sole or plaice fillets, skinned
salt and freshly ground black pepper
FRENCH DRESSING
2 tablespoons cider or wine vinegar
3 tablespoons corn oil
½ teaspoon raw cane sugar
salt and freshly ground black pepper
TO GARNISH
8 slices fresh pineapple, peeled
450 g/1 lb new potatoes, cooked

2 tomatoes, skinned and chopped roughly
fresh parsley, chopped

SERVES 4
Per serving: Energy 285 kcal/1190 kJ
Fibre 3 g

First prepare the dressing. Put all the ingredients in a screw-top jar and shake until well mixed.

Season the fish and poach in a little water until the flesh flakes. Remove with a slotted spoon and keep warm.

Put the pineapple slices for the garnish under a hot grill for a few minutes. Toss the potatoes and tomatoes in a little of the French dressing.

Arrange the fish on a plate and surround with the potatoes and pineapple. Sprinkle the tomatoes and chopped parsley on top of the fish and serve at once.

TURKEY RISOTTO

1 onion, peeled and finely chopped
1 tablespoon olive oil
350 g/12 oz cooked turkey meat
100 g/4 oz button mushrooms, wiped and sliced
1 small green pepper, cored, seeded and sliced
300 g/11 oz Italian Arborio rice
salt and freshly ground black pepper
1.25 litres/2¼ pints turkey or Vegetable stock
(page 115)

SERVES 4
Per serving: **Energy** 465 kcal/1945 kJ
 Fibre 2 g

In a large pan, gently fry the onion in the oil until tender. Add the turkey, mushrooms, green pepper, rice and seasoning. Fry gently for a further 1–2 minutes, stirring to coat the added ingredients well.

Heat the stock and add 150 ml/¼ pint simmering stock to the rice mixture. Continue to cook, stirring, until the rice absorbs the liquid, ensuring that you scrape the rice down the sides of the pan as you stir. Add another 150 ml/¼ pint of simmering stock and continue as above. Continue adding the stock until the rice is cooked. It should be fluffy and tender. Serve immediately with a crisp salad.

VARIATION
Any allowed cooked meats can be added instead of the turkey.

CHICKEN KEBABS AND MARINATED RICE

200 g/7 oz brown rice
600 ml/1 pint water
pinch salt
1 tablespoon wine or cider vinegar
1 teaspoon clear honey
1 tablespoon sunflower oil
freshly ground black pepper
ground ginger
225 g/8 oz carrots, cut in julienne strips
450 g/1 lb chicken breast, cut into bite-sized
 pieces

4 medium onions, halved
225 g/8 oz mushrooms
1 tablespoon paprika
Tabasco sauce

SERVES 4
Per serving: **Energy** 411 kcal/1720 kJ
 Fibre 7 g

Put the rice, water and salt into a saucepan. Bring to the boil and stir once. Lower the heat, cover and simmer for 25 minutes or until the rice is tender and the liquid absorbed. Remove from the heat and allow to cool.

To make the marinade, mix the vinegar, honey, 1 teaspoon of the oil, pepper and ginger in a large bowl. Add the rice and carrots. Leave to stand for 2 hours.

Thread the chicken, onions and mushrooms on to oiled skewers. In a bowl, mix together the remaining oil, paprika and a few drops of Tabasco sauce and brush over the kebabs. Place over medium hot coals or grill under high heat for 15 minutes, turning and basting occasionally.

Serve with the marinated rice and carrot.

VARIATION
For exclusion diet use bite-size pieces of lean lamb, pork or turkey.

CHICKEN KEBABS AND MARINATED RICE

DUCK WITH GINGER

2 tablespoons wheat-free soy sauce
1 tablespoon soy paste or hoisin sauce
5–6 slices root ginger, peeled and shredded
450 g / 1 lb duck meat, cut into julienne strips
2½ tablespoons sunflower oil
3 spring onions, cut into matchsticks
1 tablespoon cornflour
3 tablespoons water

SERVES 4
Per serving: **Energy** 235 kcal / 985 kJ
             Fibre negligible

In a bowl mix together the soy sauce, soy paste or hoisin sauce and ginger, then add the duck meat. Stir and turn until well blended and leave for 30 minutes.

Heat the oil in a wok or frying pan over a high heat. Add the meat and ginger mixture and stir-fry for 2 minutes. Sprinkle over the spring onions.

Blend the cornflour with the water and add to the pan. Stir and turn for 1 minute then transfer to a warmed serving dish. Serve with brown rice or rice noodles.

RABBIT CASSEROLE

2 tablespoons millet flour
salt and freshly ground black pepper
2 tablespoons sunflower oil
4 rabbit joints, about 150 g / 5 oz each
2 onions, peeled and roughly chopped
3 carrots, peeled and roughly chopped
1 small turnip or swede, peeled and roughly
    chopped

½ teaspoon mixed dried herbs
300 ml / ½ pint water

SERVES 4
Per serving: **Energy** 300 kcal / 1255 kJ
             Fibre 3 g

Preheat the oven to moderately hot (190°C, 375°F, Gas Mark 5).

Season the flour. Heat the oil in a saucepan. Coat the rabbit joints in the seasoned flour and fry gently until lightly browned all over. Remove and drain on absorbent kitchen paper, then transfer to a casserole.

Add the onions, carrots, turnip or swede and mixed herbs. Pour over the water and cover. Cook in the oven for 1½ hours.

CHICKEN WITH SESAME SAUCE

50 g / 2 oz gram flour
1½ tablespoons sesame seeds
2 teaspoons ground ginger
salt and freshly ground black pepper
1.5 kg / 3 lb oven-ready chicken, jointed and
    skinned or 4 chicken quarters, skinned
3 tablespoons sunflower oil
300 ml / ½ pint Vegetable stock (page 115)

TO GARNISH
1 tablespoon chopped parsley

SERVES 4
Per serving: **Energy** 300 kcal / 1255 kJ
             Fibre 2 g

Preheat the oven to moderately cool (150°C, 300°F, Gas Mark 3).

Mix together the flour, sesame seeds, ginger and salt and pepper to taste. Coat the chicken pieces with some of the mixture. Heat the oil in a frying pan and fry the chicken till golden. Drain on absorbent kitchen paper and place in a casserole.

Blend the remaining flour mixture with the fat left in the pan, add the stock, bring to the boil and cook, stirring, until thickened. Pour over the chicken and cook in the oven for 1½–2 hours.

Sprinkle with parsley and serve hot.

RABBIT WITH SWEET AND SOUR SAUCE

1 tablespoon cornflour
300 ml/½ pint water
4 large rabbit joints, about 150 g/5 oz each, cut into small pieces
1 small carrot, peeled and sliced
4 teaspoons clear honey
2 tablespoons wheat-free soy sauce
5 cm/2 inch piece fresh ginger, peeled and finely chopped
freshly ground black pepper

1 × 225 g (8 oz) can pineapple in natural juice, drained and roughly chopped
225 g/8 oz bean sprouts

SERVES 4
Per serving: Energy 195 kcal/815 kJ
Fibre 2 g

Blend the cornflour with a little of the water to make a smooth paste, then mix with the remaining water in a saucepan. Bring to the boil and add the rabbit, carrot, honey, soy sauce, ginger and seasoning.

Bring back to the boil, cover and simmer for 1½ hours, stirring occasionally, until the rabbit and vegetables are tender.

Stir in the pineapple pieces and serve immediately with the bean sprouts and rice, if liked.

TURKEY WITH PAPRIKA

2 tablespoons sunflower oil
450–500 g/1–1¼ lb turkey meat, cubed
2 onions, peeled and sliced
2 carrots, peeled and chopped
2 garlic cloves, peeled and crushed
1 small green pepper, cored, seeded and sliced
1 tablespoon paprika
2 tablespoons millet flour
2 tablespoons tomato purée
450 ml/¾ pint Vegetable stock (page 115)

salt and freshly ground black pepper
225 g/8 oz tomatoes, skinned and sliced

SERVES 4
Per serving: Energy 280 kcal/1170 kJ
Fibre 2 g

Preheat the oven to moderate (180°C, 350°F, Gas Mark 4).

Heat the oil in a deep frying pan, add the turkey meat and fry until well sealed. Transfer to a casserole. Add the onions, carrots, garlic and green pepper and fry gently until soft but not coloured. Stir in the paprika, flour and tomato purée and cook for 1 minute. Gradually stir in the stock and bring to the boil. Season, pour over the turkey and add the tomatoes. Mix well.

Cover the casserole and cook in the oven for about 45 minutes or until the turkey is tender. Serve with allowed noodles, rice or macaroni and salad or cooked vegetables.

DUCK WITH HONEY AND FRUIT

1 duckling, about 2¼–2¾ kg / 5–6 lb
freshly ground black pepper
1 small onion, peeled
salt
2 tablespoons clear honey
1 tablespoon boiling water
SALAD
4 crisp lettuce leaves
1 small radicchio (optional)
4 curly endive leaves (optional)
2 large peaches, sliced
1 small ripe pineapple, trimmed and sliced or
  1 × 225 g (8 oz) can pineapple slices, drained
4 sprigs watercress
6 tablespoons Vinaigrette dressing (page 117)

SERVES 4
Per serving: **Energy** 410 kcal / 1715 kJ
Fibre 1 g

Preheat the oven to 180°C, 350°F, Gas Mark 4.

Remove the giblets from the duckling. Rinse the duckling under cold running water, drain and pat dry with absorbent kitchen paper. Prick the skin all over with a fork. Sprinkle the body cavity with pepper and insert the onion. Place the bird breast-up on a rack in a roasting tin and sprinkle with salt. Roast in the centre of the oven for 30 minutes per 450 g / 1 lb.

After 1 hour of cooking, strain off the fat. Blend the honey with the water and spoon this over the duck. Continue cooking for the calculated time, basting the duck two or three times.

Check that the juices run clear when the thigh is pierced with a fine skewer, then remove the duck from the oven and cool.

Prepare individual dishes with the lettuce and fruit. Use salad leaves for the base and arrange several overlapping peach slices with a slice of pineapple on top. Fill the holes in the pineapple slices with watercress sprigs and sprinkle each salad with Vinaigrette dressing. Serve with the cold duck.

Vegetarian Dishes

For most vegetarians, milk, cheese and eggs are important sources of protein and minerals. But these are the very foods commonly found to cause allergies. Vegetarians wanting to try the exclusion diets must plan their meals very carefully, ensuring that their diet is nutritionally balanced. Soya milk, soya flour, tofu, lentils, beans and gram flour are good sources of protein for the vegetarian. These vegetable proteins should be eaten together with allowed cereals and vegetables.

QUICK VEGETABLE CURRY

2 tablespoons sunflower oil
225 g/8 oz onions, peeled and sliced
1 garlic clove, peeled and crushed
1 cooking apple, peeled, cored and chopped
2.5 cm/1 inch piece fresh root ginger, peeled and grated
2 tablespoons wheat-free curry powder
450 ml/¾ pint Vegetable stock (page 115)
salt and freshly ground black pepper
225 g/8 oz potatoes, peeled and diced
225 g/8 oz carrots, peeled and sliced
225 g/8 oz pumpkin, peeled, seeded and cubed

225 g/8 oz cauliflower florets
225 g/8 oz runner beans, sliced
50 g/2 oz sultanas
1 tablespoon grated fresh coconut

Ⓧ Ⓦ Ⓜ Ⓔ Ⓖ

SERVES 4
Per serving: **Energy** 250 kcal/1045 kJ
Fibre 9 g

Heat the oil in a large pan. Add the onions, garlic, apple and ginger and fry gently for 5 minutes, stirring occasionally. Stir in the curry powder and fry gently for a further 3 minutes, stirring constantly.

Add the stock and bring to the boil, stirring constantly, until the sauce thickens slightly. Add salt and pepper to taste, then lower the heat and simmer for 2 minutes.

Add the potatoes and carrots. Cover the pan and simmer for 10 minutes.

Add the pumpkin, cauliflower, beans and sultanas. Cover and simmer for a further 5–10 minutes or until the cauliflower is just tender but still crisp and not broken up.

Taste and adjust the seasoning. Sprinkle with the coconut and serve hot with rice, or allow to cool and serve cold as a salad.

TOFU AND VEGETABLE RISOTTO

25 g/1 oz special margarine
1 tablespoon sunflower oil
2 large onions, peeled and sliced
175 g/6 oz carrots, peeled and chopped
1 fennel bulb, about 225 g/8 oz, chopped or 1
*   garlic clove, peeled and crushed*
225 g/8 oz brown rice
600 ml/1 pint Vegetable stock (page 115)
1 bay leaf
salt and freshly ground black pepper
1 medium aubergine, about 225 g/8 oz, diced
100 g/4 oz mushrooms, sliced

100 g/4 oz frozen peas
100 g/4 oz tofu, cubed
TO GARNISH
fresh parsley

SERVES 4
Per serving: Energy 350 kcal/1465 kJ
**   Fibre**   11 g

Melt the margarine with the oil in a large heavy-based frying pan, add the onions, carrots, fennel or garlic, and fry gently for 10 minutes without browning, stirring frequently. Stir in the rice and cook for 3–4 minutes. Add the stock, bay leaf and seasoning and bring to the boil, stirring occasionally. Cover and simmer for 15 minutes.

Add the aubergine and mushrooms and stir well. Cover the pan and continue simmering for 15 minutes, stirring occasionally. Stir in the peas with a little boiling water if all the liquid has been absorbed. Add the tofu and continue cooking for a further 5–10 minutes or until the rice is tender and all the liquid has been absorbed. Adjust the seasoning and discard the bay leaf.

Pile on to a hot serving dish and garnish with parsley. Serve with a green salad.

VARIATION
You can change the vegetable ingredients according to your taste, adding courgettes, fresh or canned tomatoes, French or runner beans, nuts, peppers or pre-soaked pulses. Amend the cooking time if necessary.

BEAN, BEAN AND BEAN SALAD

175 g/6 oz dried red kidney beans or 1 × 400 g
*   (14 oz) can red kidney beans, drained*
175 g/6 oz dried black-eye beans or 1 × 400 g
*   (14 oz) can black-eye beans, drained*
1 small fennel bulb, chopped
225 g/8 oz cooked broad beans
85 ml/3 fl oz Vinaigrette dressing (page 117)

SERVES 6
Per serving: Energy 250 kcal/1045 kJ
**   Fibre**   14 g

If using dried beans, soak them overnight, or for at least 6–8 hours, keeping the 2 types separate. Drain, then boil the red kidney beans rapidly in fresh water for 10 minutes to destroy harmful toxins. Simmer for 1½–2 hours. Drain the black-eye beans and, in a separate pan, bring to the boil in fresh water and simmer for 1½–2 hours. Drain well and allow to cool.

Combine all the salad ingredients in a large earthenware bowl. Pour Vinaigrette dressing over the salad and toss thoroughly. Leave in the refrigerator for at least 1 hour before serving.

Serve with green salad and a special bread or rice.

VEGETABLE KEBABS WITH PILAFF

PILAFF
2 tablespoons sunflower oil
1 large onion, peeled and chopped
2 celery sticks, sliced
225 g/8 oz brown rice
600 ml/1 pint Vegetable stock (page 115)
50 g/2 oz seedless raisins
50 g/2 oz dried apricots, roughly chopped
1 cinnamon stick
1 bay leaf
salt and freshly ground black pepper
KEBABS
225 g/8 oz courgettes, sliced

8 small tomatoes
1 large onion, unskinned, cut into wedges
8 button mushrooms
1 green pepper, cored, seeded and cut into 8
1 tablespoon sunflower oil
1 tablespoon thyme leaves

SERVES 4
Per serving: **Energy** 385 kcal/1610 kJ
                       Fibre 12 g

For the pilaff, heat the oil in a pan. Add the onion and celery and fry gently for 5 minutes until golden brown. Add the rice and cook for 1 minute, stirring constantly. Pour on the stock, then add the raisins and apricots.

Bring to the boil, stirring occasionally, then add the cinnamon, bay leaf and seasoning. Lower the heat, cover, and simmer for 30 minutes or until the rice is tender and the stock has been absorbed.

For the kebabs, blanch the courgettes in boiling water for 1 minute, then drain. Thread the vegetables alternately on to 4 large kebab skewers.

Mix the oil with the thyme and seasoning to taste, then brush over the vegetables. Cook on a barbecue or under the grill for 5–10 minutes until cooked through, turning and basting from time to time.

Spoon the pilaff into a warmed shallow serving dish and arrange the kebabs on top.

DHAL

225 g/8 oz red lentils
600 ml/1 pint water
1 bay leaf
salt and freshly ground black pepper
1 tablespoon sunflower oil
1 onion, peeled and finely chopped
1 clove garlic, crushed
½ teaspoon ground ginger or 1 teaspoon grated
  root ginger (optional)

½ teaspoon ground coriander
½ teaspoon ground cumin

SERVES 4
Per serving: **Energy** 205 kcal/860 kJ
                       Fibre 6 g

Place the lentils in a saucepan and add the water, bay leaf and seasoning. Cover the pan and bring to the boil. Simmer for 15–30 minutes until the lentils are swollen and the water has been absorbed to give a thickish purée.

Heat the oil in a clean pan and fry the onion, garlic and root ginger, if used, for 5 minutes until lightly browned. Add the spices and cook for 1 minute. Add the cooked lentil purée and cook gently for 5 minutes.

Serve hot with rice, or as an accompaniment to curry, or cold with a salad.

ABOVE: DAHL; BELOW: VEGETABLE KEBABS
WITH PILAFF

BEANS WITH PAPRIKA

350 g/12 oz haricot beans, soaked overnight
2 tablespoons sunflower oil
1 large onion, peeled and sliced
1 garlic clove, peeled and crushed
1 tablespoon paprika
50 g/2 oz canned pimiento, sliced
1 × 400 g (14 oz) can tomatoes, roughly
  chopped, with their juices
150 ml/¼ pint water

SERVES 4
Per serving: **Energy**   320 kcal/1340 kJ
                    Fibre   23 g

Drain the haricot beans, and cook in fresh water for 45 minutes or until almost tender. Drain.

Heat the oil in a large pan and gently fry the onion and garlic until soft. Add the paprika and cook, stirring, for 2–3 minutes.

Add the beans, pimiento, tomatoes and water. Bring to the boil, cover and simmer gently for about 10 minutes. Serve with rice and freshly cooked vegetables.

LENTILS WITH TOMATOES

225 g/8 oz brown or green lentils
1 × 400 g (14 oz) can tomatoes, roughly
  chopped with their juices
600 ml/1 pint water
1 onion, peeled and chopped
1 tablespoon chopped fresh oregano, marjoram
  or basil
salt and freshly ground black pepper

TO GARNISH
1 tablespoon chopped fresh marjoram or parsley

SERVES 4
Per serving: **Energy**   190 kcal/795 kJ
                    Fibre   8 g

Put the lentils in a saucepan and pour in the tomatoes and water. Add the onion, herbs and seasoning. Cover the pan and bring to the boil.

Simmer gently for 1–1¼ hours until the lentils are tender and most of the liquid has evaporated, but the mixture is still moist. Stir occasionally towards the end of the cooking time to stop the lentils sticking.

Sprinkle with chopped fresh marjoram or parsley and serve with special bread and salad.

NOODLES WITH SPINACH AND YOGURT

225 g/8 oz Buckwheat noodles (page 49)
salt
50 g/2 oz special margarine
1 onion, peeled and chopped
225 g/8 oz packet frozen spinach, thawed
150 ml/¼ pint goat's yogurt
¼ teaspoon ground nutmeg
salt and freshly ground black pepper

SERVES 3
Per serving: **Energy**   345 kcal/1445 kJ
                    Fibre   6 g

Cook the noodles in a large pan of lightly salted boiling water for 3–5 minutes until they are just tender.

Make the sauce. Heat the margarine in a large saucepan and fry the onion for 5 minutes. Add the spinach, yogurt, nutmeg and seasoning and bring to the boil.

Drain the noodles and add them to the spinach mixture. Cook gently, stirring occasionally, until the noodles are heated through. Serve at once.

SPAGHETTI WITH RATATOUILLE

275–350 g / 10–12 oz buckwheat spaghetti or
  Buckweat noodles (page 49)
Ratatouille (page 71)

SERVES 4
Per serving: **Energy** 310 kcal / 1295 kJ
             Fibre   4 g

In a large saucepan bring 1.2 litres/2 pints lightly salted water to the boil. Add the spaghetti or noodles and cook until just tender but firm to bite.

Heat the Ratatouille and serve with the drained spaghetti or noodles.

VARIATION
If your diet allows wheat, you can use ordinary spaghetti, which is egg- and milk-free.

LENTIL PATTIES

2 tablespoons sunflower oil plus extra for
  shallow frying
½ fennel bulb, about 100 g / 4 oz, chopped
50 g / 2 oz celeriac, peeled and chopped
1 carrot, peeled and chopped
225 g / 8 oz brown lentils
450 ml / ¾ pint water
salt and freshly ground black pepper
4 tablespoons gram flour
½ teaspoon ground ginger
½ teaspoon ground cumin
1 teaspoon wheat-free curry powder
Yogurt dressing (page 117) or Tomato sauce I
  or II (page 116)

SERVES 6
Per serving: **Energy** 270 kcal / 1130 kJ
             Fibre   7 g

Heat 2 tablespoons of the oil in a large pan. Add the fennel, celeriac and carrot and fry gently until they begin to soften.

Add the lentils, water and seasoning. Bring to the boil, then lower the heat, cover and simmer for about 1 hour until the lentils are soft and all the liquid is absorbed.

Add half the flour and the spices to the pan and mix well. Continue to cook gently for 2–3 minutes, stirring constantly.

Turn the mixture on to a plate and leave until cool enough to handle. Divide it into 18 and form each one into a patty, about 1 cm / ½ inch thick. Coat with the remaining flour. Heat a little oil in a frying pan and fry the lentil patties, a few at a time, until crisp and golden brown, turning once.

Serve the patties on a bed of rice topped with the Yogurt dressing or Tomato sauce.

Salads & Vegetables

Vegetables and salads provide us with vitamins, minerals and fibre. To maintain their nutritional value you should always:

1 Select fresh, firm, undamaged vegetables and salads. Alternatively, you could buy these foods frozen.

2 Avoid peeling any vegetable – or peel it very thinly. Keep any waste/peelings for making stock (page 115).

3 Never use bicarbonate of soda as it destroys vitamins.

4 Boil vegetables in the minimum of water and cook until tender, but not soft. They are better underdone than overdone.

5 Stir-fry vegetables in as little vegetable oil as possible. This is a good way of cooking with the minimum vitamin and mineral loss.

6 Try some of the more unusual vegetables available to give variety to your diet: Jerusalem artichokes, calabrese, cassava, celeriac, eddoes, kohl rabi, mangetouts, okra (ladies' fingers), plantain, salsify and sweet potatoes.

FRUIT AND CABBAGE SALAD

450 g / 1 lb white cabbage, finely shredded
50 g / 2 oz dried apricots, finely chopped
75 g / 3 oz raisins
4 spring onions, chopped
1 green pepper, cored, seeded and chopped
½ bunch radishes, sliced
Yogurt dressing (page 117)

SERVES 6
Per serving: **Energy** 95 kcal/400 kJ
                Fibre 5 g

Place all the ingredients in a large bowl and mix well. Just before serving, pour the Yogurt dressing over the salad and toss the ingredients together well.

ABOVE: FRUIT AND CABBAGE SALAD; BELOW: CARROT AND RAISIN SALAD (P. 102)

BEAN SPROUT SALAD

100 g / 4 oz dried red kidney beans
4 peaches, peeled and sliced
225 g / 8 oz bean sprouts
4 sticks celery, sliced
2 tablespoons Vinaigrette dressing (page 117)
1 tablespoon parsley, chopped

SERVES 5
Per serving: **Energy**   115 kcal / 480 kJ
                  Fibre   7 g

Cover the beans with water and bring to the boil. Simmer for 2 minutes, then turn off the heat and leave to soak for 2 hours. After soaking, cover the beans with fresh water and bring to the boil. Boil rapidly for 10 minutes. Turn the heat down and simmer for 45-60 minutes. When cooked, drain and leave to cool.

In a bowl combine the cooled beans, peach slices, bean sprouts and celery. Add the dressing and parsley and toss well.

ITALIAN SALAD

½ head curly endive, separated into leaves
1 head chicory, sliced into rings
1 fennel bulb, sliced into rings
1 small head radicchio, separated into leaves
8 radishes, sliced if large
4 tablespoons Vinaigrette dressing (page 117)
salt and freshly ground black pepper

SERVES 4
Per serving: **Energy**   90 kcal / 375 kJ
                  Fibre   2 g

Put all the ingredients in a salad bowl, toss well with the dressing, then taste and adjust the seasoning. Serve immediately.

OKRA RICE

1 tablespoon sunflower oil
450 g / 1 lb long-grain rice
600 ml / 1 pint allowed Meat stock (page 114)
pinch salt
2 chillis, seeded and cut into fine strips
1 red pepper, cored, seeded and chopped
275 g / 9 oz okra, trimmed

SERVES 8
Per serving: **Energy**   230 kcal / 960 kJ
                  Fibre   6 g

Heat the oil in a pan, add the rice and fry for 2 minutes. Add the stock, salt, chillis and red pepper, stirring well. Cover and cook for 5 minutes.

Add the okra. Cover and continue to cook over a low heat for 12–15 minutes, until the rice has absorbed all the stock and is tender but still firm.

Serve hot. Okra rice is tasty served with meat kebabs.

RICE RING

1 tablespoon sunflower oil
225 g/8 oz brown rice
750 ml/1¼ pints water
1 green pepper, cored, seeded and chopped
50 g/2 oz dried apricots, soaked and sliced
50 g/2 oz dried prunes, soaked, stoned and
    sliced
50 g/2 oz black olives, halved and stoned
75 g/3 oz walnuts, roughly chopped (optional)
salt and freshly ground black pepper

SERVES 4
Per serving: **Energy** 380 kcal/1590 kJ
             Fibre 11 g

Preheat the oven to moderate (180°C, 350°F, Gas Mark 4).

Heat the oil in a large pan. Stir in the rice and cook, stirring, for 1 minute. Add the water. Bring to the boil, cover and simmer for 20 minutes.

Stir in the green pepper, apricots and prunes. Continue to simmer, covered, for about 20 minutes or until the rice is cooked and the liquid absorbed. Stir in the olives and walnuts, if used, and season to taste.

Turn the mixture into a greased 900 ml (1½ pint) ring mould and cook in the oven for 30 minutes. Turn out and serve hot or cold. Fill the centre with Ratatouille (page 71) or a crisp green salad if preferred.

VARIATION
For exclusion diet omit the walnuts.

HERB SALAD

1 garlic clove, peeled and halved
1 cos lettuce
100 g/4 oz lamb's lettuce
1 bunch watercress
1 punnet mustard and cress
1 bunch rocket
1 bunch chives
1 bunch parsley
1 bunch basil
1 bunch mint
2 oranges, peeled, sliced and quartered

DRESSING
2 tablespoons olive oil
1 tablespoon wine vinegar
2 garlic cloves, peeled and crushed
1 teaspoon soft brown sugar

SERVES 8
Per serving: **Energy** 45 kcal/190 kJ
             Fibre 2 g

Use the cut garlic clove to rub round the inside of a large bowl, then discard. Wash and prepare the salad greens, using as many listed above as are available. Chop the chives and parsley and strip the leaves from the basil and mint, discarding the stems. Place the salad greens and herbs in the salad bowl with the orange pieces and mix well.

To make the dressing, place all the ingredients in a bowl and whisk together, or place in a screw-top jar and shake well. Just before serving, pour the dressing over the salad and toss well. *Illustrated on page 70.*

VARIATION
For exclusion diets omit the oranges.

POLENTA

1.5 litres / 2½ pints water
½ teaspoon salt
300 g / 11 oz coarse-grained corn meal

SERVES 6
Per serving: **Energy** 190 kcal / 795 kJ
Fibre 1 g

Put the water in a large heavy saucepan and bring to the boil. Add the salt and reduce the heat so that the water is just simmering. Add the corn meal in a thin stream, stirring with a wooden spoon. Cook for 20 minutes, stirring constantly. The polenta is done when it leaves the sides of the pot as you stir.

Serve it piping hot with any meat, stew or casserole. It is particularly good with rabbit and other game meats.

VARIATIONS
Pour the cooked polenta on to a large wooden block or a flat dish and allow to cool. When cold, cut into 1 cm / ½ inch thick slices and fry in oil. This is a delicious accompaniment to roasts or grilled meats or vegetable dishes.

Alternatively, cut into thicker slices and toast under a hot grill until lightly browned on both sides. Spread with a ripe strong goat's cheese and serve with a salad.

RATATOUILLE

1 large aubergine, sliced
salt
4 tablespoons olive oil
2 medium onions, peeled and thinly sliced
1 garlic clove, peeled and crushed
750 g / 1½ lb ripe tomatoes, peeled, seeded and
	quartered
½ teaspoon dried oregano
450 g / 1 lb courgettes, sliced
1 large green pepper, cored, seeded and thinly
	sliced
1 large red pepper, cored, seeded and thinly
	sliced

freshly ground black pepper
TO GARNISH
freshly chopped parsley

SERVES 6
Per serving: **Energy** 115 kcal / 480 kJ
Fibre 3 g

Sprinkle the aubergine slices with salt and leave to drain for 30 minutes in a colander. Wash and dry well on absorbent kitchen paper.

Heat the oil in a large saucepan, add the onions, garlic, tomatoes and oregano and cook gently for 3–4 minutes until the juices flow from the tomatoes.

Add the remaining vegetables and season. Stir well. Bring to the boil, stirring constantly, then lower the heat, cover with a lid and cook gently, stirring occasionally, for 30 minutes or until the vegetables are soft. Remove from the heat, taste for seasoning and garnish with parsley. Serve the Ratatouille hot as a vegetable dish or chilled as a starter.

HERB SALAD (P.69)

GNOCCHI

750 g/1½ lb potatoes suitable for mashing
pinch salt
50 g/2 oz potato flour
50 g/2 oz buckwheat flour
TO GARNISH
special margarine
chopped parsley

SERVES 6
Per serving: **Energy** 145 kcal/605 kJ
                   Fibre 3 g

Boil the potatoes, unpeeled, in abundant water. When cooked, peel as soon as they can be handled. Purée while still warm and add salt to taste.

Gradually add flour to the potato purée and knead. The dough should be smooth and still slightly sticky. You may not need to add all of the flour.

Shape the dough into tiny sausages, drop them into a pan of boiling water and cook for 3–5 minutes after they have risen to the surface. Drain and serve dotted with margarine and sprinkled with parsley.

VARIATIONS
If your diet allows, serve with 25 g/1 oz grated cheese sprinkled over and lightly browned under a hot grill.

Gnocchi are equally good with hot Tomato sauce (page 116) poured over.

MANGETOUT WITH TAMARI DRESSING

750 g/1½ lb mangetout, topped and tailed
3 tablespoons cider vinegar
4 tablespoons sesame or olive oil
1 tablespoon chives
1 tablespoon Tamari sauce
1 parsley sprig, chopped
salt and freshly ground black pepper

SERVES 6
Per serving: **Energy** 110 kcal/460 kJ
                   Fibre 4 g

Place the mangetout in a pan with just enough water to cover. Bring to the boil, then lower the heat and cook gently for 5–10 minutes, depending on the ripeness and freshness of the mangetout (very young pods will need only about 2 minutes).

To make the dressing, beat together the remaining ingredients until well blended.

Drain the mangetout thoroughly and transfer to a serving bowl. Pour the dressing over while they are still warm. Leave to stand for at least 5 minutes before serving, or allow to cool and serve cold.

BRUSSELS SPROUTS WITH CHESTNUTS

350 g/12 oz chestnuts
25 g/1 oz special margarine
150 ml/¼ pint Vegetable stock (page 115)
450 g/1 lb Brussels sprouts, trimmed
salt and freshly ground black pepper

SERVES 4
Per serving: **Energy** 190 kcal/795 kJ
                   Fibre 7 g

Slit the chestnuts with a sharp knife. Place in a pan of cold water, bring to the boil and simmer for 3 minutes. Remove the chestnuts and peel off their outer and inner skins.

Heat the margarine in a small pan, add the chestnuts and cook for 5 minutes, stirring occasionally. Add the stock, bring to the boil, cover and simmer for 20 minutes.

Add the Brussels sprouts, adding more liquid if necessary to just cover the vegetables. Season and cook for a further 5–10 minutes until the Brussels sprouts are tender. Drain the Brussels sprouts and chestnuts. Transfer to serving dish.

POTATO AND ONION BAKE

25 ml / 1 fl oz sunflower oil
2 Spanish onions, peeled and coarsely chopped
  or sliced into rings
6 large potatoes, peeled and sliced
salt and freshly ground black pepper

SERVES 6
Per serving: **Energy** 165 kcal/690 kJ
           Fibre   3 g

Preheat the oven to moderately hot (190°C, 375°F, Gas Mark 5).

Heat the oil in a frying pan, add the onions and cook for 5 minutes. Fill an ovenproof dish with alternate layers of sliced potato and onion, seasoning each layer with salt and pepper and finishing with a layer of fried onion.

Cook for 1 hour or until the potatoes are tender. This is a good accompaniment to baked or grilled fish.

CHINESE CABBAGE WITH SAFFRON

1 small Chinese cabbage
½ cucumber, peeled and chopped
300 ml / ½ pint allowed Meat stock (page 114)
1 tablespoon chopped red pepper
15 g / ½ oz special margarine
½ onion, peeled and finely chopped
salt and freshly ground black pepper
pinch saffron
1 teaspoon cornflour

SERVES 4
Per serving: **Energy** 55 kcal/230 kJ
           Fibre   1 g

Quarter the cabbage, remove any coarse outer leaves and thick stalks. Cut the leaves into wide strips.

Place the cabbage and cucumber in a pan with the meat stock. Bring to the boil, then lower the heat and cook over a low heat, for about 8 minutes. Add the red pepper and cook for a further 2 minutes.

Melt the margarine in a pan, add the onion and cook for 3–4 minutes. Add to the cabbage mixture, season and add the saffron, mixing well. Dissolve the cornflour in a little water and add to the cabbage mixture, blending well. Cook, stirring, for about 2 minutes. Serve immediately.

VEGETABLE FRITTERS

50 g / 2 oz potato flour
50 g / 2 oz brown rice flour
pinch salt
2 teaspoons egg replacer
150 ml / ¼ pint water or milk substitute
1 small aubergine, thinly sliced
salt
2 courgettes, thinly sliced
16 onion rings
8 cauliflower florets

1 red pepper, cored, seeded and cut into thin
  rings
corn oil for deep frying

SERVES 8
Per serving: **Energy** 80 kcal / 335 kJ
  Fibre 1 g

First make the batter: sift the flours and salt together into a bowl and make a well in the centre. Add the egg replacer and whisk, gradually adding the water or milk substitute until the batter is smooth.

Lay the aubergine slices on absorbent kitchen paper, sprinkle with salt and leave for 15 minutes. Pat dry, turn the slices and repeat for the other side.

Dip the vegetables in batter, shake off excess, and deep fry in hot oil (180°C/ 350°F) for 5 minutes, until tender. Drain on absorbent kitchen paper and serve immediately.

TOMATOES WITH FENNEL AND DILL

4 small heads fennel
olive oil for frying
salt and freshly ground black pepper
450 g / 1 lb tomatoes, skinned and sliced
3 tablespoons chopped dill

SERVES 4
Per serving: **Energy** 40 kcal / 165 kJ
  Fibre 3 g

Cut the fennel into very thin slices. Brush the bottom of a non-stick pan with a little oil and stew the fennel gently, stirring often, until almost soft. Add salt and pepper to taste.

Add the tomatoes to the fennel and continue cooking gently for 5 minutes, stirring occasionally without breaking up the tomatoes. When cooked, stir in the chopped dill and transfer to a dish to cool. Serve cold but not chilled.

TOMATOES WITH FENNEL AND DILL

Desserts

Fruit features in nearly all of these desserts to give a refreshing and light finish to the meal. Fruits, like vegetables, add vitamins, minerals and fibre to the diet.

Nowadays there is a huge variety of fruits available in the shops.

If you haven't done so already, why not try some of the more exotic ones such as custard apple, fresh dates and figs, guava, kiwi fruit (a most attractive fruit – ideal to decorate desserts with), lychees, mango, mangosteen, passion fruit, paw paw, sharon fruit and rambutan.

APPLE CHARLOTTE WITH BREAD

450 g/1 lb cooking apples, peeled, cored and
  sliced
2 tablespoons water
25 g/1 oz soft brown sugar
100 g/4 oz fresh special breadcrumbs
2 tablespoons demerara sugar
½ teaspoon ground cinnamon
25 g/1 oz special hard margarine

SERVES 4
Per serving: **Energy** 240 kcal/1005 kJ
              Fibre 3 g

Preheat the oven to moderate (180°C, 350°F, Gas Mark 4).

Put the sliced apples into a saucepan with the water and simmer for 10–15 minutes until tender. Add the brown sugar.

Mix the breadcrumbs with the demerara sugar and cinnamon.

Place half the sweetened apple in a greased pie dish. Cover with half the crumb mixture, then the rest of the apple and finally top with the remaining crumb mixture. Dot the surface with margarine.

Cover the dish with greased greaseproof paper or foil and bake for 30–40 minutes.

FRUIT CRUNCH

1 kg/2 lb plums, halved and stoned
75 g/3 oz demerara sugar
50 g/2 oz Rice Krispies or cornflakes, lightly
  crushed

SERVES 4
Per serving: **Energy** 175 kcal/730 kJ
              Fibre 6 g

Preheat the oven to moderately hot (190°C, 375°F, Gas Mark 5).

Put the plums in a shallow baking dish. Mix the sugar with the cereal and sprinkle over the fruit. Bake for 45 minutes.

VARIATION
Use any fruit allowed in your diet instead of plums.

PEARS IN CASSIS

300 ml / ½ pint apple juice
100 g / 4 oz blackcurrants, stalks removed
honey to taste
1 cinnamon stick
4 pears
1 teaspoon arrowroot

SERVES 4
Per serving: Energy 65 kcal / 270 kJ
              Fibre   3 g

Pour the apple juice into a pan, then add the blackcurrants, honey and cinnamon. Heat gently until the honey has dissolved, then bring to the boil. Boil for 1 minute.

Peel the pears, leaving the stalks attached. Put the pears in the pan, submerging them as much as possible in the blackcurrant mixture. Cover and cook gently for about 20 minutes until the pears are tender, turning occasionally.

Lift the pears from the pan and transfer to a serving bowl. Discard the cinnamon stick.

Blend the arrowroot with a little cold water, then pour into the blackcurrant mixture. Bring to the boil, then lower the heat and simmer for 1 minute until the sauce thickens, stirring constantly. Pour over the pears. Serve hot or cold.

SPICED PEACH PANCAKES

PANCAKE BATTER
50 g / 2 oz potato flour
50 g / 2 oz brown rice flour
2 teaspoons egg replacer
300 ml / ½ pint water or milk substitute
sunflower oil for frying
FILLING
1 teaspoon mixed spice
4 ripe peaches, peeled and sliced
50 g / 2 oz special margarine
50 g / 2 oz raw cane sugar

1 teaspoon grated lemon rind
1 teaspoon grated orange rind
1 tablespoon lemon juice
2 tablespoons orange juice

SERVES 4
Per serving: Energy 270 kcal / 1130 kJ
              Fibre   2 g

Make the pancake batter by blending all the batter ingredients in a liquidizer or food processor for 1 minute until well mixed. Heat a little oil in a small non-stick frying pan. Pour sufficient batter into the pan to just cover the base. Cook for 1–2 minutes, then turn or toss the pancake and cook on the second side. Remove from the pan. Keep warm while making more pancakes. (This quantity makes 8–12 pancakes.)

For the filling, sprinkle the mixed spice over the sliced peaches in a bowl. Heat the margarine and sugar in a frying pan, and add the spiced peach slices. Turn them to coat, add the rinds and juices and simmer for a few minutes. Fill the hot pancakes with the peach mixture and fold into quarters. Serve with the pan juices.

OATY FRUIT CRUMBLE

75 g / 3 oz special hard margarine
100 g / 4 oz brown rice flour
50 g / 2 oz demerara sugar
40 g / 1½ oz rolled oats
FILLING
450 g / 1 lb fresh damsons, washed and trimmed
1 medium pear, peeled, cored and sliced
25 g / 1 oz raw cane sugar

SERVES 4
Per serving: **Energy** 385 kcal / 1610 kJ
 Fibre 7 g

Preheat the oven to moderately hot (190°C, 375°F, Gas Mark 5).

For the topping, cut the margarine into pieces and rub into the flour until it resembles fine breadcrumbs. Stir in the demerara sugar and oats.

Put the damsons and pear into a 1.2 litre (2 pint) pie dish. Stir in the sugar. Spoon over the crumble topping and bake in the oven for 30–35 minutes until the filling is soft when tested with a skewer. Serve with a custard sauce or plain goat's yogurt if allowed in diet.

VARIATIONS
Use crushed cornflakes or crushed biscuits allowed in your diet in place of rolled oats for the topping. Use fruits such as rhubarb and apple, plum, apricot and ginger.

BAKED BANANAS

50 g/2 oz special margarine
1 tablespoon brown sugar
finely grated rind and juice of 1 orange
1 tablespoon lemon juice
pinch ground mixed spice
4 large bananas, halved lengthways
2 tablespoons desiccated coconut

SERVES 4
Per serving: **Energy** 230 kcal/960 kJ
          Fibre 4 g

Preheat the oven to moderate (180°C, 350°F, Gas Mark 4).

Put the margarine, sugar, orange rind and juice, lemon juice and spice in a saucepan and heat gently, stirring to dissolve the sugar.

Put the bananas in a baking dish and pour over the spiced mixture. Sprinkle with the coconut. Bake for 30 minutes.

BLACKBERRY STUFFED APPLES

BLACKBERRY STUFFED APPLES

4 large cooking apples
225 g/8 oz blackberries
4 tablespoons raw cane sugar
1 tablespoon chopped mint
4 tablespoons water

SERVES 4
Per serving: **Energy** 165 kcal/690 kJ
          Fibre 7 g

Preheat the oven to moderate (180°C, 350°F, Gas Mark 4).

Remove the cores from the apples, making a large hole for the stuffing. Make a shallow cut through the skin around the centre of each apple to prevent the skins bursting.

To make the stuffing, mix the blackberries with the sugar and mint. Place the apples in a baking dish and divide the stuffing equally between the apples, pressing it well down into the centres.

Spoon any remaining stuffing around the apples, then spoon over the water.

Bake in the oven for 45 minutes or until the apples are tender. Serve hot.

VARIATION
For exclusion diet use 225 g/8 oz blackcurrants instead of the blackberries.

APPLE PUDDING

50 g / 2 oz special margarine
25 g / 1 oz sugar
2 eggs, separated
50 g / 2 oz potato flour
1 teaspoon ground cinnamon
250 g / 9 oz cooking apples, peeled and grated
1 tablespoon chopped walnuts
5 tablespoons apple juice
25 g / 1 oz dates, stoned and chopped
pinch salt

SERVES 4
Per serving: **Energy** 265 kcal / 1110 kJ
Fibre 2 g

Heat the oven to moderate (180°C, 350°F, Gas Mark 4).

Cream together the margarine and sugar. Beat in the egg yolks. Fold in the potato flour, cinnamon, apple, walnuts, apple juice and dates. Beat the egg whites with the salt until stiff and fold into the apple mixture. Spoon into a greased baking dish and bake for 45 minutes.

VARIATION
Use 225 g / 8 oz grated carrot instead of the grated apple.

RHUBARB COBBLER

750 g / 1½ lb rhubarb, trimmed and cut into 1
    inch pieces
150 ml / ¼ pint water
sugar to taste
1 teaspoon ground ginger
SCONE TOPPING
175 g / 6 oz rice flour
1½ teaspoons wheat-free baking powder
1 teaspoon ground ginger
40 g / 1½ oz special margarine

40 g / 1½ oz soft brown sugar
5–6 tablespoons milk substitute
1 tablespoon demerara sugar

SERVES 4
Per serving: **Energy** 310 kcal / 1295 kJ
Fibre 7 g

Preheat the oven to hot (200°C, 400°F, Gas Mark 6).

Put the rhubarb in a saucepan with the water and bring to the boil. Cover and simmer gently until tender but not mushy. Sweeten to taste and stir in the ginger. Fill a pie dish or casserole with the rhubarb, allowing space for the topping.

To make the topping, sift the flour, baking powder and ginger into a bowl and rub in the fat until the mixture resembles breadcrumbs. Stir in the brown sugar and add sufficient milk to mix to a soft dough. Roll out the dough on a floured surface to about 1 cm / ½ inch thick and cut into 4 cm / 1½ inch rounds. Arrange the rounds in an overlapping circle around the edge of the pie dish over the rhubarb. Brush the dough rounds with milk substitute and sprinkle with demerara sugar.

Bake in the oven for about 30 minutes or until the topping is well risen and golden brown. Serve hot.

VARIATION
Any stewed fruit or combination of fruits can be used for a cobbler and the scone topping may be flavoured to complement the fruit.

APPLE AND MINT SNOW

1 kg/2 lb cooking apples, peeled, cored and
    sliced
6 tablespoons water
3 tablespoons clear honey
4 large sprigs mint
2 teaspoons egg replacer

SERVES 4
Per serving: **Energy** 135 kcal/565 kJ
                Fibre 4 g

Put the apples in a pan and add 2 table-spoons of the water and the honey. Add the mint, reserving the top leaves for decoration. Cover and cook gently for about 15 minutes until the apples are cooked to a pulp, stirring occasionally. Discard the mint. Rub through a plastic sieve or work to a purée in an electric blender or food processor. Leave to cool.

Combine the remaining water with the egg replacer and whisk until stiff. Fold into the apple purée. Spoon into a serving bowl or individual dishes or glasses. Decorate with the reserved mint leaves. Serve chilled but do not make more than 1–2 hours before it is needed.

VARIATION
Instead of the apples use 1 kg/2 lb rhubarb, washed and cut into 5 cm/2 inch pieces.

APPLE AND MINT SNOW

TROPICAL FRUIT SALAD

1 large pineapple
2 passion fruit
2 kiwi fruit, peeled and sliced
1 mango, peeled and sliced
3 tablespoons pineapple juice

SERVES 4
Per serving: **Energy** 70 kcal/295 kJ
                   Fibre 3 g

Cut off the top of the pineapple. Carefully pull away 2 or 3 leaves for decoration. Cut out the flesh of the pineapple by cutting inside the skin with a long, sharp knife and scooping out the flesh with a spoon. Slice the flesh into bite-sized pieces, discarding the core.

Halve the passion fruit and spoon out the flesh. Mix all the fruits together in a bowl with the pineapple juice. Spoon them into the pineapple shell and chill.

Just before serving, decorate with the pineapple leaves. Serve with Creamy topping (page 119).

PINEAPPLE SORBET

flesh of 1 large pineapple
2 teaspoons Gelozone (optional)
300 ml / ½ pint unsweetened pineapple juice
100 ml / 3½ fl oz water
2 teaspoons egg replacer, mixed with 4
   tablespoons water

SERVES 6
Per serving: **Energy** 50 kcal/210 kJ
                   Fibre negligible

Purée the pineapple flesh in a blender, then pass through a sieve into a large bowl.

Mix the Gelozone to a smooth paste with a little of the fruit juice, then stir into the remaining juice and the water in a saucepan and bring to the boil. Boil for 2 minutes. Allow to cool, then add to the fruit purée.

Pour into a shallow container or ice trays and freeze for 2 hours, or until almost set. Then transfer to a food processor or blen-

der and reduce to a mush.

Whisk the egg replacer and water mixture until stiff, then fold into the half-frozen fruit sorbet. Pour back into the freezer container and freeze until solid. For a very smooth sorbet, purée twice more during the freezing.

The Gelozone keeps the sorbet smooth, but can be omitted if it is to be eaten within 24 hours of making.

RHUBARB ICE CREAM

675 g / 1½ lb rhubarb, cut into 5 cm / 1 inch
   pieces
2 tablespoons water
50 g / 2 oz sugar, or to taste
2 teaspoons egg replacer mixed with 2
   tablespoons water
300 ml / ½ pint milk substitute

SERVES 5
Per serving: **Energy** 80 kcal/335 kJ
                   Fibre 2 g

Put the rhubarb in a saucepan with the water and half the sugar. Bring to the boil and simmer until the rhubarb is soft. Lift out the rhubarb with a slotted spoon, leaving the juice in the saucepan.

Blend the rhubarb to a smooth purée. Add the rest of the sugar if necessary. Boil the juice to reduce to 175 ml/6 oz. Cool slightly and stir in the egg replacer. Simmer for 2–3 minutes, beating constantly. Fold in the rhubarb purée and the milk substitute. Pour into a shallow tin and put in the freezer. Freeze for 45 minutes, then tip the ice cream into a food processor or blender and process for 30–60 seconds before returning to the tin. Repeat twice.

OGEN JELLY

1 Ogen melon, weighing at least 300 g/11 oz
juice of 1 lemon
15 g/½ oz Gelozone
100 ml/4 fl oz water
50 g/2 oz sugar
TO DECORATE
225 g/8 oz strawberries, sliced
caster sugar

SERVES 4
Per serving: Energy 75 kcal/315 kJ
Fibre 1 g

Halve the melon. Discard the seeds, then scoop out the flesh and blend to a purée with the lemon juice.

Mix the Gelozone with a little of the water to form a smooth paste. Stir in the remainder of the water, add the sugar and bring to the boil for two minutes. Cool slightly, then add the melon purée.

Pour the jelly mixture into a 600 ml (1 pint) ring mould and chill until set.

Dip the mould into hot water for a few seconds to loosen the jelly from the sides. Turn on to a serving dish. Pile strawberries into the ring and dredge with caster sugar.

INDIVIDUAL CUSTARD TARTS

225 g/8 oz Sweet shortcrust pastry (page 86)
450 ml/¾ pint milk substitute
1 vanilla pod
2 teaspoons egg replacer
1 teaspoon honey (optional)
TO DECORATE
grated nutmeg or quarter slices of kiwi fruit, peeled

MAKES 12
Each: Energy 85 kcal/355 kJ
Fibre negligible

Prepare and bake blind the tart cases as for Individual fruit tarts (page 84).

Put the milk in a saucepan, add the vanilla pod and bring to the boil, then allow to cool slowly. Remove the vanilla pod. Mix 4 tablespoons of the vanilla-flavoured milk with the egg replacer, then add the remaining milk. Stir in the honey if used. Return to the saucepan and cook, stirring, for 2–3 minutes, then allow to cool slightly. Fill the tarts with the custard and allow to set.

To serve, sprinkle the individual tarts with a little grated nutmeg or arrange quarter slices of kiwi fruit on top.

CHERRY FLAN

175 g/6 oz Sweet shortcrust pastry (page 86)
FILLING
25 g/1 oz cornflour
25 g/1 oz caster sugar
1 egg, beaten
300 ml/½ pint milk substitute
vanilla flavouring
225 g/8 oz fresh cherries, trimmed and stoned or
*   1 × 425 g (15 oz) can natural cherries,*
*   drained*

GLAZE
2 teaspoons arrowroot
150 ml/¼ pint water
1 teaspoon sugar

SERVES 6
Per serving: Energy 190 kcal/795 kJ
            Fibre   1 g

Preheat the oven to hot (200°C, 400°F, Gas Mark 6).

Line a 20 cm (8 inch) fluted flan ring or flan dish with the pastry. Prick the base. Place the dish on a baking sheet. Chill for 10 minutes then bake blind in the oven for 20 minutes. Allow to cool.

Meanwhile, make the confectioner's custard by blending the flour, sugar and egg together in a basin. Heat the milk, then pour it on to the mixture, stirring well. Return the mixture to the saucepan, reheat until boiling and simmer for 2 minutes, stirring all the time. Add the vanilla flavouring. Cover and allow to cool.

Spread the cooled custard over the base of the baked flan case. Arrange the cherries neatly over the custard.

To make the glaze, blend the arrowroot with a little water in a bowl. Add the sugar and the remaining water. Pour the mixture into a saucepan and bring to the boil, stirring all the time until the glaze becomes transparent. Brush over the fruit.

Serve the flan chilled.

INDIVIDUAL FRUIT TARTS

225 g/8 oz Sweet shortcrust pastry (page 86)
275 g/10 oz prepared allowed fresh fruit or
*   canned fruit in natural juice (pineapple,*
*   grapes, cherries, melon, peaches)*
100 g/4 oz apricot or cherry jam (additive-free,
*   sugar-reduced variety)*
1 tablespoon water

MAKES 12
Each: Energy 85 kcal/355 kJ
       Fibre   1 g

Preheat the oven to hot (200°C, 400°F, Gas Mark 6).

Roll out the pastry to a thickness of 5 mm/¼ inch. Cut out the tart cases with a pastry cutter, put them in a patty tin and prick the bases. Fill them with baking beans. Place on a baking sheet and bake blind for about 15 minutes or until crisp and golden. Remove the baking beans and allow to cool.

When cold, fill the tarts with the fresh or canned fruit, attractively arranged.

Make a jam glaze by heating the jam (use apricot for light coloured or mixed fruits and cherry for red fruits) and water together in a saucepan over gentle heat until the jam softens. Sieve the mixture. If the glaze needs to be thicker, return it to the saucepan and boil until it is of suitable coating consistency.

Glaze the tarts and serve on their own or with Creamy topping (page 119).

INDIVIDUAL FRUIT TARTS

Baking

You will find the recipes in this chapter the most unusual of all the recipes in the book. 'How can I bake without eggs, wheat and milk?', you may be asking yourself.

Surprisingly enough, it can be done and you will produce appetizing and interesting dishes, though you should be prepared for slightly different tastes. All the recipes in this section have been tried and enjoyed. Using the flours described on page 23 rather than wheat will give you baked goods with less volume; they will tend to be heavier and more crumbly; they also tend to stick to the tins more, so use either non-stick tins or line baking tins with non-stick silicone paper (especially when making biscuits) rather than greaseproof paper.

Once you have mastered the technique of using these flours you can try adapting some of your own recipes. The special breads do not keep well for more than 2 days. Therefore freeze your bread (ready sliced) and only take from your freezer the amounts needed.

The egg replacer recommended on page 22 does work. It can be used whenever an egg is called for in a recipe. However, it does not have the same nutritional value.

We have used dried yeast in the recipes, but fresh yeast can be used if preferred, remembering that 15 g/½ oz dried yeast = 25 g/1 oz fresh yeast.

SWEET SHORTCRUST PASTRY

50 g/2 oz special hard margarine
100 g/4 oz brown rice flour
75 g/3 oz finely grated cooking apple or quince
1 teaspoon sugar (optional)

Total recipe: **Energy** 775 kcal/3245 kJ
                  Fibre 10 g

Put the flour in a bowl and rub in the margarine until it resembles fine breadcrumbs. Add the grated apple or quince and sugar, and knead into a ball.

Use as required. Use extra rice flour for rolling out and grease the cooking tins with special margarine.

For cold dishes, bake blind at 220°C, 425°F, Gas Mark 7 for 20–25 minutes.

SHORTCRUST PASTRY

200 g / 7 oz cornflour or sago flour
90 g / 3½ oz special hard margarine

Ⓧ Ⓦ Ⓜ Ⓔ Ⓖ

Total recipe: **Energy** 1365 kcal / 5710 kJ
Fibre negligible

Sift together the flour and salt. Rub in the fat until the mixture resembles fine breadcrumbs. Add sufficient water to mix until it clings together.

Chill for at least 20 minutes before rolling out and using as required.

TORTILLAS AND FLATBREADS

150 g / 5 oz cornmeal (maize flour)
pinch salt
pinch chilli powder (optional)
about 175 ml / 6 fl oz tepid water

Ⓧ Ⓦ Ⓜ Ⓔ Ⓖ

SERVES 4
Per serving: **Energy** 140 kcal / 585 kJ
Fibre negligible

Place the cornmeal, salt and chilli, if used, in a bowl. Add the water gradually, kneading to form a smooth soft dough. Divide into 8, cover and leave to stand for an hour.

Place each piece of dough between 2 sheets of cling film and roll into cakes 13 cm (5 inches) in diameter.

Heat an ungreased heavy frying pan. When hot, place a tortilla in the pan. Cook for about 1 minute or until golden speckles appear on the surface. Turn the tortilla and cook the other side for 1–1½ minutes. Wrap in a warm cloth and keep hot while cooking the remainder.

VARIATIONS
TORTILLA CHIPS Cut each uncooked tortilla into 6 equal triangles. Deep fry in corn oil at 190°C / 375°F until golden and crisp. Do not overcook. Drain on absorbent kitchen paper.

These make excellent nibbles, or you can serve them to accompany dips, dishes such as Guacamole (page 38), or soups.
CORNMEAL FLATBREAD Add 1 teaspoon wheat-free baking powder to the cornmeal flour before mixing with the water. Make the dough straight away into thicker cakes. Cook in a frying pan with a little oil (1 tablespoon per flatbread) until golden brown on both sides. Dry on absorbent kitchen paper. *Illustrated on pages 88–9.*
FLATBREAD WITH CUMIN Add 1 teaspoon ground cumin or cumin seeds to the cornmeal flatbread mixture before adding the water. Serve the flatbread hot or cold. *Illustrated on pages 88–9.*

RICE AND RYE BREAD

1 teaspoon sugar
300 ml / ½ pint tepid water
15 g / ½ oz dried yeast (1 tablespoon)
175 g / 6 oz brown rice flour
175 g / 6 oz rye flour
1 teaspoon salt
25 ml / 1 fl oz sunflower oil

MAKES 1 450 g (1 lb) loaf
Per loaf: **Energy**   1585 kcal / 6630 kJ
           Fibre   19 g

Preheat the oven to hot (200°C, 400°F, Gas Mark 6).

Dissolve the sugar in the water, sprinkle on the yeast and leave in a warm place until it begins to froth.

Sift the flours and salt into a large bowl, add the oil and yeast mixture. Beat to a thick pouring consistency. With suitable margarine (page 22), grease a 450 g (1 lb) loaf tin. Pour the bread mixture into the prepared tin and seal inside a large polythene bag. Leave the dough to rise in a warm place for about an hour or until it has doubled in size.

Bake in the oven for 25–30 minutes. Remove the partially baked bread from the tin and place on a baking sheet. Bake for a further 15–20 minutes to make a nice crust.

SOYA AND RICE BREAD

10 g / ¼ oz dried yeast (2 teaspoons)
1 teaspoon honey
150 ml / 5 fl oz tepid water
275 g / 10 oz brown rice flour
50 g / 2 oz soya flour
½ teaspoon salt
1 teaspoon egg replacer mixed with 2
   tablespoons water

MAKES 1 450 g (1 lb) loaf
Total recipe: **Energy** 1255 kcal/5250 kJ
              Fibre 33 g

Preheat the oven to hot (200°C, 400°F, Gas Mark 6).

Mix the yeast, honey and water together and leave to froth in a warm place.

Sift the rice flour, soya flour and salt together in a bowl. Make a hollow in the centre and add the egg replacer mixture. Add the yeast mixture when ready. Stir to make a smooth stiff batter, adding extra water as needed. With a suitable margarine, grease a 450 g (1 lb) loaf tin. Pour the bread mixture in, enclose the tin in a polythene bag and leave to rise in a warm place for an hour or until doubled in size. Bake in the oven for 30–45 minutes.

SODA BREAD

50 g / 2 oz soya flour
275 g / 10 oz brown rice flour
½ teaspoon salt
¾ teaspoon cream of tartar
¾ teaspoon bicarbonate of soda
1 tablespoon sunflower oil
275 ml / 9 fl oz milk substitute

MAKES 1 loaf
Total recipe: **Energy** 1320 kcal/5525 kJ
              Fibre 31 g

Preheat the oven to hot (200°C, 400°F, Gas Mark 6).

Put the flours, salt, cream of tartar and bicarbonate of soda in a bowl. Mix the oil with the milk substitute and combine with the dry ingredients to form a soft dough. Form into a round shape and place on a greased tray. Bake for 40–45 minutes.

FROM LEFT TO RIGHT: FLATBREAD WITH CUMIN AND CORNMEAL FLATBREAD (P. 87); SODA BREAD; SOYA AND RICE BREAD

BROWNIES

50 g/2 oz special margarine
100 g/4 oz soft brown sugar
1 teaspoon egg replacer mixed with 2
  tablespoons water
¼ teaspoon natural vanilla essence
50 g/2 oz brown rice flour
1 teaspoon wheat-free baking powder (page 97)
50 g/2 oz desiccated coconut

MAKES 16 brownies
Each: Energy 80 kcal/335 kJ
       Fibre 1 g

Preheat the oven to moderately hot (190°C, 375°F, Gas Mark 5).

Line the base of a shallow 20 cm (8 inch) square tin with silicone paper. Melt the fat in a saucepan over gentle heat, then mix in the sugar and stir until dissolved. Cool slightly and beat in the egg replacer mixture and vanilla essence. Sift the flour together with baking powder and mix in thoroughly. Stir in the coconut and pour into the prepared tin. Bake in the oven for about 30 minutes or until set, but not hard.

Cut into 16 squares while still hot, then allow to cool in the tin. When cold, lift out carefully and store in an airtight tin or plastic container.

FRUIT SCONES

50 g/2 oz buckwheat flour
150 g/5 oz brown rice flour
2 teaspoons wheat-free baking powder (page 97)
50 g/2 oz special margarine
50 g/2 oz dried fruit
100 g/4 oz grated apple, with skin
about 6 tablespoons milk substitute

MAKES 15 scones
Each: Energy 85 kcal/355 kJ
       Fibre 1 g

Preheat the oven to very hot (230°C, 450°F, Gas Mark 8).

Sift the flours and baking powder together and rub in the margarine. Add the dried fruit and grated apple and mix together to a soft dough with the milk substitute.

Drop the mixture with a spoon on to a greased baking sheet. Bake in the oven for 15–20 minutes and cool on a wire tray.

FRUIT MALT LOAF

15 g/½ oz dried yeast (1 tablespoon)
75 ml/2½ fl oz tepid water
1 teaspoon honey
100 g/4 oz brown rice flour
100 g/4 oz rye flour
100 g/4 oz sultanas
25 g/1 oz special margarine
50 g/2 oz malt extract

25 g/1 oz black treacle
1 tablespoon clear honey to glaze

MAKES 1 loaf
Total recipe: Energy 1325 kcal/5545 kJ
            Fibre 19 g

Preheat the oven to moderately hot (200°C, 400°F, Gas Mark 5).

Mix the yeast, water and honey together and leave to froth in a warm place.

Mix the flours and sultanas together in a warm bowl. Put the margarine, malt extract and black treacle in a pan and heat gently until the margarine has melted. Leave to cool for 5 minutes.

Add the yeast and treacle to the dry ingredients and mix to a soft dough. Transfer to a greased 450 g (1 lb) loaf tin, cover with a damp cloth and leave in a warm place for about 1 hour or until double in size.

Bake in the oven for 45 minutes. Turn out on to a wire tray, brush with honey, then leave to cool.

PARKIN

100 g/4 oz brown rice flour
300 g/11 oz medium oatmeal
1 teaspoon ground ginger
100 g/4 oz special margarine
100 g/4 oz honey
100 g/4 oz black treacle
4 tablespoons milk substitute
½ teaspoon bicarbonate of soda

Total recipe: **Energy** 2875 kcal/12030 kJ
Fibre 11 g

Preheat the oven to moderately cool (160°C, 325°F, Gas Mark 3).

Put the flour, oatmeal and ginger in a bowl and mix well. Put the margarine, honey and black treacle in a pan and heat gently until the margarine has melted. Add to the dry ingredients and mix well.

Heat the milk until tepid, stir in the soda, then add to the flour mixture and beat well. Pour the mixture into a greased 18 cm (7 inch) square cake tin.

Bake for approximately 1 hour. Leave to cool in the tin for 10 minutes, then turn out on to a wire tray to cool completely.

Store in an airtight tin for 3–4 days before cutting.

FRUIT CAKE

15 g/½ oz dried yeast (1 tablespoon)
300 ml/½ pint tepid pineapple juice
50 g/2 oz soya flour
50 g/2 oz millet flour
225 g/8 oz brown rice flour
3 teaspoons wheat-free baking powder (page 97)
2 teaspoons ground cinnamon
2 tablespoons sunflower oil
450 g/1 lb dried mixed fruit

100 g/4 oz chopped dates
2 cooking apples, peeled and chopped

Total recipe: **Energy** 2745 kcal/11485 kJ
Fibre 77 g

Preheat the oven to moderate (180°C, 350°F, Gas Mark 4). Sprinkle the yeast on to the pineapple juice. Leave to froth.

Put the flours, baking powder and cinnamon in a bowl. Stir in the oil.

Blend the fruit in a food processor or blender. Add the fruit purée and the frothy pineapple juice mixture to the flour and stir well to a sloppy mixture, adding more juice if needed.

Spoon the mixture into a greased 23 cm (9 inch) cake tin and bake for about 1 hour. Allow to cool for a few minutes in the tin, then transfer to a wire tray.

PINEAPPLE UPSIDE-DOWN CAKE

TOPPING
40 g/1½ oz raw cane sugar
*1 × 225 g (8 oz) can round pineapple pieces in
    natural juice, drained and juice reserved*
4–5 fresh cherries, stoned (optional)
CAKE MIXTURE
90 g/3½ oz potato flour
25 g/1 oz soya flour
75 g/3 oz brown rice flour
2 apples, grated, with skins
50 g/2 oz raw cane sugar

*1 tablespoon wheat-free baking powder (page
    97)*
*juice from the pineapple, made up to 200 ml/⅓
    pint with more pineapple juice if necessary*
1 tablespoon sunflower oil

Total recipe: **Energy** 1430 kcal/5985 kJ
Fibre 17 g

Preheat the oven to hot (200°C, 400°F, Gas Mark 6).

Grease a straight sided, 23 cm (9 inch) round ovenproof dish with special margarine (page 00). Arrange the pineapple pieces on the base and sprinkle the sugar over. Cut the cherries in half, if used, and arrange them between the pineapple pieces.

Put the ingredients for the cake mixture in a food processor and blend until creamy. Spread over the pineapple and cherries.

Bake in the oven for 30 minutes. Leave to cool for 5 minutes then turn out on to a serving plate.

This cake can be served hot with a suitable sauce for dessert if liked.

CAROB AND BUCKWHEAT CAKE

175 g/6 oz buckwheat flour
40 g/1½ oz carob powder
1½ teaspoons wheat-free baking powder
175 g/6 oz soft brown sugar
175 g/6 oz special margarine
1½ tablespoons water
3 eggs
FILLING
25 g/1 oz (scant) carob powder, sieved
3 tablespoons clear honey
50 g/2 oz special margarine

2 tablespoons powdered soya milk
1 tablespoon cold water
TOPPING
icing sugar (made by grinding sugar)

Total recipe: **Energy** 3780 kcal/15815 kJ
Fibre 10 g

Preheat the oven to moderate (180°C, 350°F, Gas Mark 4).

Sift the flour, carob and baking powder into a large mixing bowl. Add the sugar, margarine and water and beat thoroughly for 1 minute. (This is best done in an electric mixer, at top speed.) Add the eggs and continue beating for 1 minute, occasionally scraping the mixture away from the sides of the bowl.

Divide the mixture between two greased and lined 15 cm (6 inch) sandwich tins and smooth the tops. Bake in the oven for 35

minutes or until a hot skewer inserted into the centres comes out clean. Leave to cool in the tins for a few minutes, then turn out on to a wire tray to cool completely.

To make the filling, put the carob powder, honey and margarine in a heavy-based saucepan and melt gently, stirring. Remove from the heat. Dissolve the powdered milk in the cold water and stir into the flour mixture. Leave the mixture to cool completely and thicken, then use it to sandwich the cakes together.

Sprinkle the top with icing sugar.

CAROB AND BUCKWHEAT CAKE

PINEAPPLE AND CARROT CAKE

100 g / 4 oz special margarine
100 g / 4 oz sugar
1 teaspoon ground cinnamon
2 teaspoons egg replacer mixed with 4
  tablespoons water
75 g / 3 oz raw carrot, finely grated
75 g / 3 oz pineapple, finely chopped
1–2 tablespoons pineapple juice
225 g / 8 oz self-raising flour

| **Total recipe:** | **Energy** | 1960 kcal / 8200 kJ |
| | **Fibre** | 11 g |

Preheat the oven to moderate (180°C, 350°F, Gas Mark 4).

Cream the margarine and sugar together in a bowl until pale and fluffy. Beat in the ground cinnamon. Gradually add the egg replacer mixture, beating well after each addition. Stir in the carrot, pineapple and juice. Sift over the flour and fold into the creamed mixture.

Put the mixture into a greased 20 cm (8 inch) cake tin and bake for 1 hour.

The flavour of the cake improves if kept for 1 day before eating.

APPLE CAKE

100 g/4 oz potato flour
100 g/4 oz brown rice flour
½ teaspoon ground cinnamon
½ teaspoon mixed spice (optional)
½ teaspoon bicarbonate of soda
100 g/4 oz special margarine
100 g/4 oz currants
175 g/6 oz sultanas
225 g/8 oz cooking apples, peeled, cored and coarsely grated

2 teaspoons egg replacer mixed with 4 tablespoons water

Total recipe: **Energy** 2015 kcal/8430 kJ
Fibre 25 g

Preheat the oven to moderate (180°C, 350°F, Gas Mark 4).

Sift the flours, spices and soda together. Rub the margarine into the flour until it resembles fine breadcrumbs. Mix in the fruits and bind with the egg replacer mixture.

Turn into a greased and lined 20 cm (8 inch) round cake tin, level the top and bake for 1¼–1½ hours or until the cake is firm to the touch and a skewer inserted in the centre comes out clean. Turn out and cool on a wire tray.

SPONGE CAKE

175 g/6 oz special margarine
75 g/3 oz sugar
3 teaspoons egg replacer mixed with 6 tablespoons water
175 g/6 oz brown rice flour
40 g/1½ oz buckwheat flour
1½ teaspoons wheat-free baking powder
3 tablespoons additive-free or Freezer jam (page 119)

TO DECORATE
icing sugar

Total recipe: **Energy** 2460 kcal/10295 kJ
Fibre 16 g

Preheat the oven to hot (200°C, 400°F, Gas Mark 6).

Cream the fat and sugar until soft and fluffy. Gradually add the egg replacer mixture. Lightly mix in the flours and baking powder, adding a little extra tepid water if the mixture seems stiff.

Divide between 2 × 15 cm (6 inch) greased sponge tins. Bake for 12–15 minutes.

Turn out on to a wire tray to cool.

Spread one sponge with jam and place the other on top. Dust with icing sugar or cover with margarine cream icing.

MILLET AND RICE SAVOURY BISCUITS

100 g/4 oz millet flour
100 g/4 oz brown rice flour
¼ teaspoon salt
2 teaspoons wheat-free baking powder (page 97)
50 g/2 oz special margarine
100 ml/3½ fl oz water

Ⓧ Ⓧ Ⓦ Ⓜ Ⓔ Ⓖ

MAKES 20 biscuits
Each: Energy 55 kcal/230 kJ
      Fibre negligible

Preheat the oven to moderately hot (190°C, 375°F, Gas Mark 5).

Combine the flours, salt and baking powder in a bowl. Rub in the margarine. Add the water to make a soft dough.

Roll out to 1 cm (½ inch) thick. Cut into rounds, arrange on a greased baking sheet and bake in the oven for 10–15 minutes.

VARIATION
Top with blobs of tomato, spinach and carrot purées to make Traffic light biscuits.

SPICE BISCUITS

100 g/4 oz special margarine
50 g/2 oz soft brown sugar
50 g/2 oz mashed potato, sieved
175 g/6 oz brown rice flour
50 g/2 oz sultanas
1 teaspoon mixed spice

Ⓧ Ⓦ Ⓜ Ⓔ Ⓖ

MAKES 20 biscuits
Each: Energy 85 kcal/355 kJ
      Fibre 1 g

Preheat the oven to moderate (180°C, 350°F, Gas Mark 4).

Cream together the butter and sugar until smooth and fluffy, then beat in the potato.

Add the flour, sultanas and spice and mix well. Turn on to a lightly floured surface and roll out to 5 mm (¼ inch) thick. Using a 7 cm (2½ inch) cutter, cut out rounds and place them on greased baking sheets.

Bake in the oven for 15–20 minutes until golden brown.

JAM SQUARES

175 g/6 oz rolled oats
225 g/8 oz brown rice flour
225 g/8 oz special margarine
100 g/4 oz soft brown sugar
50 g/2 oz dried fruit, chopped
1 teaspoon cinnamon
½ teaspoon bicarbonate of soda
5 tablespoons additive-free cherry jam

MAKES 28 squares
Each: Energy 135 kcal/565 kJ
      Fibre 1 g

Preheat the oven to hot (200°C, 400°F, Gas Mark 6).

Place all the ingredients except the jam in a large bowl. Beat the mixture until it is crumbly. Reserving 3–4 tablespoons of the mixture, press the rest into a well greased 32 × 23 cm (13 × 9 inch) cake tin. Spread evenly with jam and sprinkle over the reserved mixture. Bake for 30 minutes until golden. Cool in the tin. Cut into squares.

MILLET FLAPJACKS

100 g/4 oz special margarine
50 g/2 oz demerara or light brown sugar
2 tablespoons golden syrup
225 g/8 oz millet flakes

MAKES 18 flapjacks
Each: Energy 105 kcal/440 kJ
         Fibre   negligible

Preheat the oven to moderate (180°C, 350°F, Gas Mark 4).

Put the margarine, sugar and syrup into a saucepan over a gentle heat until the fat and sugar have melted. Add the millet flakes, mixing thoroughly.

Grease a 20 cm (8 inch) square sandwich tin. Spoon in the millet mixture and spread flat with a palette knife. Bake in the centre of the oven for about 30 minutes or until evenly golden brown.

Cool in the tin for about 5 minutes. Mark into 18 portions. Allow to cool completely, then remove the portions from the tin and store in an airtight tin.

MILLET FLAPJACKS AND COCONUT COOKIES

COCONUT COOKIES

100 g/4 oz special margarine
50 g/2 oz golden syrup
50 g/2 oz demerara sugar
1 level teaspoon bicarbonate of soda
50 g/2 oz desiccated coconut
75 g/3 oz millet flakes
100 g/4 oz brown rice flour

MAKES 24 cookies
Each: **Energy** 85 kcal/355 kJ
       Fibre 1 g

Preheat the oven to moderate (160°C, 325°F, Gas Mark 3).

Put the margarine, syrup and sugar into a large saucepan. Stir over a low heat until the fat and sugar have melted. Remove from the heat, add the bicarbonate of soda and stir well to dissolve. (The mixture rises up the pan during this stage.) Add the rest of the ingredients and blend thoroughly.

Cool slightly, then gather the mixture together and roll into about 24 balls.

Put the balls on 2 greased baking sheets, allowing plenty of space for the mixture to spread out during cooking.

Bake in the centre of the oven for 15–20 minutes or until golden brown. Leave on the trays until almost cold, then transfer to a wire tray to cool completely.

RICE FLOUR SHORTBREAD

150 g/5 oz brown rice flour
25 g/1 oz ground rice
50 g/2 oz sugar
100 g/4 oz special margarine

MAKES 8 pieces
Each: **Energy** 195 kcal/815 kJ
       Fibre 2 g

Preheat the oven to moderate (160°C, 325°F, Gas Mark 3).

Sift the flour and ground rice into a bowl and stir in the sugar. Add the margarine and rub in, then knead to make a smooth dough. Do not allow the dough to become sticky. Cover and chill for 30 minutes.

Press the dough into an 18 cm (7 inch) round or fluted flan ring on a greased baking sheet. Prick all over with a fork,

then mark the plain round into wedges. Chill for 15 minutes.

Bake in the oven for 35–40 minutes or until pale golden. Allow to cool slightly on the baking sheet, then transfer to a wire tray to cool completely.

VARIATION
Use 50 g/2 oz raisins in place of 25 g/1 oz of the sugar.

HOMEMADE WHEAT-FREE BAKING POWDER

100 g/4 oz rice flour
50 g/2 oz bicarbonate of soda
50 g/2 oz tartaric acid

Mix the ingredients together and sieve several times. Store in a screw-top jar.

The recipes in this book were tested with commercial wheat-free baking powder.

Babies' & Children's Recipes

The recipes here include some which can be used when baby first starts solids and others which are for the older infant. These recipes are not coded for use on the exclusion diet, as we do not recommend that children try the exclusion diet *except* with dietetic supervision.

Remember that for all children, including the allergic child, it is important to establish good and nutritionally sound eating habits.

1 Do not use salt when cooking for babies and young children.

2 Use fresh foods rather than the commercially prepared alternatives.

3 Do not give sugar or oversweetened foods. Try using dried fruit, when appropriate, to sweeten puddings.

4 Water on its own, or diluted pure fruit juice (1 part juice to 3 parts water) is preferable to squashes or fizzy drinks.

5 Avoid salty or sweet snack foods (it's the between-meal sugary foods and drinks that do the most harm to teeth), and give fresh or dried fruit and raw vegetables instead.

6 Start your children on wholegrain and wholemeal foods rather than the refined alternatives.

7 Don't use too much fat in cooking or on bread.

8 If sweets and chocolates need to be given, then give them as occasional treats or at parties. See page 105 for ideas on party foods.

Establishing a sensible eating pattern early on in childhood is worthwhile and it will make the management of a healthy diet easier as the child grows older.

TODDLER'S SHISH KEBABS

450 g/1 lb leg of lamb, veal or pork fillet
1 × 150 g (5 oz) carton plain unsweetened
   yogurt
1 tablespoon finely chopped parsley
pinch dried marjoram

SERVES 6
Per serving: **Energy**   150 kcal/630 kJ
                    Fibre   negligible

Cut the meat into small cubes. Blend the yogurt, parsley and marjoram. Place the meat and the yogurt mixture together in a bowl. Cover and leave to marinate for 30 minutes. Thread the meat closely together on skewers, choosing the smallest pieces of meat for the toddler's portion (At this stage you can sprinkle the adult portions with salt and freshly ground black pepper.)

Place under a preheated grill, turning the skewers at intervals, until the meat is well cooked, about 20–25 minutes. Serve with jacket baked potatoes and green salad, using any remaining marinade as a dressing for the salad.

This makes an ideal party dish for older children.

CHEESE WITH VEGETABLE RICE

2 teaspoons sunflower oil
25 g/1 oz brown rice
150 ml/¼ pint hot Vegetable stock (page 115)
25 g/1 oz chopped red pepper
25 g/1 oz sliced courgette
25 g/1 oz French beans, trimmed and halved
15 g/½ oz grated cheese

SERVES 1
Per serving: **Energy**   255 kcal/1065 kJ
                    Fibre   3 g

Heat the oil in a saucepan and add the rice. Fry gently for 1–2 minutes and add the hot vegetable stock. Cook for 15 minutes. Add the prepared vegetables and cook for a further 15 minutes or until the rice is cooked. If the mixture dries out, add more stock or water. Serve with the grated cheese on top. *Illustrated on page 104.*

RICE AND RAISIN PUDDING

600 ml/1 pint milk
50 g/2 oz rice, rinsed under cold water
25 g/1 oz special margarine
75 g/3 oz raisins
additive-free jam, to decorate

SERVES 4
Per serving: **Energy**   235 kcal/985 kJ
                    Fibre   1 g

Preheat the oven to cool (150°C, 300°F, Gas Mark 2).

Bring the milk to the boil in a saucepan and stir in the rice. Pour into a lightly greased 900 ml (1½ pint) ovenproof dish.

Dot with special margarine.

Bake for 2 hours, until set. Stir the pudding after 1 hour to separate the grains. Leave to cool a little. Stir in the raisins and serve topped with a swirl of the jam.

Party foods

It is difficult for mothers of children with newly diagnosed food allergies to envisage hosting a party without brightly coloured jellies, ice cream, and 'pop', or salty, sugary and highly coloured snacks, sausages and sandwiches; the (all too often) half-eaten birthday cake and the sweet- and chocolate-filled 'swag bag' to finish off with.

At your next party as well as trying some of the party recipes on the following pages, try these party ideas:

1 Rice cakes or allowed bread topped with seed spread and fruit or with Freezer jam (page 119) or any other allowed savoury topping. To make them look colourful decorate with fresh fruit and raw vegetables.

2 Homemade popcorn – but don't add too much salt or sugar.

3 Fresh fruit salad.

4 Shish kebabs (page 103).

5 Jelly (page 83).

6 Dried fruits and pieces of raw vegetables.

MEAT BALL PARCELS

100 g/4 oz belly pork, rind removed, finely
   minced
100 g/4 oz lean pork meat, finely minced
25 g/1 oz fresh special breadcrumbs moistened
   with a little water
25 g/1 oz cornflour
300 ml/½ pint apple juice
1 tablespoon corn oil
1 large onion, peeled and thinly sliced
2 dessert apples, cored and sliced

MAKES 15–20 small meat balls
SERVES 5
Per serving: Energy 195 kcal/815 kJ
             Fibre 1 g

Preheat the oven to moderately hot (190°C, 375°F, Gas Mark 5).

Put the pork meats and breadcrumbs in a bowl and mix. Roll into small meat balls.

Mix the cornflour with a little of the apple juice to a smooth paste, then add the remaining juice. Heat in a saucepan and cook for 3–4 minutes. Add more juice if it becomes too thick.

Heat the oil in a frying pan and lightly fry the onion until golden brown.

CHEESE WITH VEGETABLE RICE (P. 103)

Cut out 5 × 20 × 20 cm (8 × 8 inch) pieces of aluminium foil. In the centre of each arrange 3 sausages topped with a little of the fried onion, sliced apple and the apple sauce. Gather the edges of the foil together and seal to form little parcels. Put in the oven for 20–30 minutes or until the sausages are cooked. Uncover the parcels for the last 2 minutes to brown.

These little Meat ball parcels are ideal as a hot party dish for children. Serve with Fried potato shapes (page 106). *Illustrated on pages 108–9.*

FRIED POTATO SHAPES

1 kg/2 lb large potatoes, peeled
corn oil for frying

Total recipe: **Energy** 1520 kcal/6360 kJ
Fibre 18 g

Cut the potatoes into even slices and stamp out shapes with tiny cocktail cutters. Rinse and drain very well.

Heat the oil in a deep-fat fryer or large saucepan until it is hot enough to turn a stale bread cube golden brown in 30 seconds (190°C/375°F). Add the potato shapes and fry until crisp and golden brown round the edges. Drain well on absorbent kitchen paper and serve hot with Meat ball parcels (page 105).

Children love these fancy 'chips' for a party and they take little time and trouble to prepare. *Illustrated on pages 108–9.*

ICE CREAM

600 ml/1 pint milk
1 tablespoon honey (or to taste)
3–4 tablespoons corn oil

Total recipe: **Energy** 830 kcal/3475 kJ
Fibre nil

Combine the ingredients well, then freeze in an ice cream maker. Alternatively, put the mixture in the freezer until it begins to set, then process in a blender or food processor. Return to the freezer and repeat the process twice more for a smooth ice cream.

VARIATIONS
FRUIT ICE CREAM Add about 275 g/10 fl oz fruit juice or fruit purée to the mixture before freezing.
CAROB ICE CREAM Add 2 tablespoons carob powder to the mixture before freezing.

FROZEN BANANAS

2 teaspoons vitamin C powder
300 ml/½ pint water
4 bananas, peeled
1 tablespoon carob powder mixed with a little
    hot corn oil

SERVES 4
Per serving: **Energy** 80 kcal/335 kJ
Fibre 3 g

Dissolve the vitamin C powder in the water and dunk the bananas in it. This will help prevent browning. Insert a lollipop stick in each banana then put on a tray and freeze.

When frozen, dip the ends of the bananas in the carob paste and allow to set. Return the bananas to the freezer and serve them frozen.

VARIATION
Dip the ends of the bananas in some thawed Freezer jam (page 119) instead of the carob.

SNACK CRUNCH

100 g/4 oz special margarine
100 g/4 oz cherry or apricot additive-free jam
25 g/1 oz cornflakes, crushed
175 g/6 oz millet flakes
150 g/6 oz raisins or chopped dates

MAKES 500 g/1¼ lb
Total recipe: **Energy** 1990 kcal/8325 kJ
             Fibre 21 g

Preheat the oven to moderate (170°C, 325°F, Gas Mark 3).

Combine the margarine and jam in a large saucepan and cook over low heat, stirring constantly until the mixture is well blended and smooth. Remove from the heat and stir in the cornflakes and millet. Mix until well coated, then transfer the mixture to an ungreased 30 × 25 cm (12 × 10 inch) baking sheet. Bake in the oven for 35–40 minutes or until golden. Stir occasionally. Remove from the oven, add the raisins and mix well. Transfer to a cold ungreased baking sheet to cool. Store in an airtight container.

VARIATION

Add 25 g/1 oz chopped nuts, if allowed, or 25 g/1 oz Rice Krispies to the crunch instead of the cornflakes.

FRUIT SALAD ON A STICK WITH COCONUT CREAM

COCONUT CREAM
3 tablespoons desiccated coconut
6 tablespoons boiling water
1 teaspoon arrowroot
FRUIT SALAD
1 teaspoon vitamin C powder
150 ml/¼ pint apple juice
1 pear, peeled, cored and cut into 8 pieces
2 small firm bananas, peeled and quartered
2 slices fresh or canned pineapple, quartered
8 stoned cherries or seedless grapes

TO DECORATE
2 tablespoons clear honey
desiccated coconut

SERVES 4
Per serving: **Energy** 150 kcal/630 kJ
             Fibre 3 g

To make the Coconut cream, mix the desiccated coconut with the boiling water. Leave to stand for 30 minutes. Liquidize, then strain through a sieve, pressing on the coconut to extract the flavour. Mix the arrowroot with a little of the coconut juice to a smooth paste, then add the remaining coconut juice. Bring to the boil and cook for 3–4 minutes. Keep warm.

To make Fruit salad on sticks, mix the vitamin C powder with the apple juice. Add the fruit to the apple juice and stir until evenly coated to prevent unnecessary discoloration of the fruit.

Drain the fruit thoroughly and thread alternately on to 4 kebab skewers or several cocktail sticks. Put the fruit kebabs on the rack of the grill pan. Brush with melted honey and sprinkle with the desiccated coconut.

Place under a preheated grill and cook for 3–4 minutes until lightly golden. Serve immediately with the coconut cream decorated with toasted desiccated coconut, if you wish.

The fruit can be varied according to taste and the salad sticks can also be served uncooked without the coconut cream. Makes a colourful children's party dish. *Illustrated on pages 108–9.*

TOFFEE APPLES

4 dessert apples (Cox's or russets)
450 g / 1 lb sugar
150 ml / ¼ pint water

MAKES 4 apples
Each apple: **Energy** 480 kcal/2010 kJ
              Fibre   1 g

Wash the apples and dry them thoroughly. Push a stick into the core of each apple.

Put the sugar and water in a pan over gentle heat and stir frequently. When the sugar has completely dissolved, turn up the heat and let the syrup boil rapidly until it turns a golden caramel. Remove from the heat.

Quickly swirl each apple in the caramel and place it on a lightly oiled sheet of glass or a mirror. Leave until set. If the caramel hardens before all the apples are coated, return it to the heat to melt.

When the caramel has set, wrap the toffee apples in coloured cellophane. Best eaten on the day of making when the caramel is hard.

Apples with a waxy shine are not suitable for this recipe, because the toffee will not stick to the apple.

TOFFEE APPLES